The Illustrated Library of

NATURE

VOLUME 3

ANIMAL
WORLD–(cont.)

BIRDS

The American Museum of Natural History

Cooperated in the publication
of this edition.

The Illustrated Library of
NATURE

THIS PICTORIAL ENCYCLOPEDIA of natural history and ecology depicts the relationships of all living organisms to each other and between them and their environments. Original manuscript from the *Doubleday Nature Programs* plus new articles and illustrations are included in this edition.

H. S. STUTTMAN CO., INC., Publishers
New York, N. Y., 10016

Contents

ANIMAL WORLD–(cont.)

BIRDS

Smaller Rodents

WITH THE EXCEPTION of man, the brown or Norway rat is probably the most widespread and adaptable of all mammals. Everywhere that man has gone, the rat has followed. Rats thrive in unsanitary surroundings, may attack people and are known to communicate infectious disease. What they do not eat, they often despoil. Their tracks are often seen in flour which they have caused to be spilled or in mud around the waterfront when the tide goes out. They have five toes on the hind foot and four toes on the forefoot. Their small, black, hard dung pellets are easily recognized, as are the holes they gnaw through wooden buildings. They make extensive networks of tunnels underground to which they retire when threatened.

The common house mouse is perhaps the rat's closest rival for the title of most numerous rodent. It too now inhabits most of the world. The holes which it gnaws in buildings, its soft fluffy nests, which may be discovered almost anywhere, and its small dark droppings are so well known that most of us have more experience at tracking than we realize.

There are so many different types of rats and mice in the world that it is impossible even to list them all here. They have adapted to so many different kinds of life that they are found wherever life can be supported. So called "domestic" rats and mice are destructive, yet there are others which do no harm and are interesting to observe. As in the case of laboratory animals, mice can even prove beneficial to man. Most of them have four toes on the front feet and five toes on the hind feet. When a mouse or rat bounds along in soft snow, its tail will leave a drag mark.

Falconry, or hunting with falcons, is one of the oldest sports in the world, and it is still practiced today in many places. The falcon is set free to hunt, and it comes back to its owner with the prey. In this picture, however, the **peregrine falcon**, or duck hawk, is bringing back a pigeon to its nest and waiting young. This hawk, the swiftest flying of all, is found throughout the world. Although it was once common near New York City, it is now rare in North America.

(above, left)
A favorite pet in many homes, the common **hamster** is actually Syrian in origin. In the wild state it burrows under the ground for shelter and protection.

(above, right)
A well-nibbled ear of corn often provides evidence that a **squirrel** is in the region. Visitors to city parks have no need to search for them, for they usually appear willingly, hopeful of a snack of bread crumbs or nuts.

While discussing rodents used as laboratory animals, we should mention the hamsters. These interesting little creatures are found in their wild state in Europe, Asia and Asia Minor. The golden hamsters with which we are most familiar come from Syria. Widely used in research, these hamsters are also excellent pets for children, for they are easily handled and require little care. In their wild state, hamsters live in underground burrows.

The gray squirrel, originally an American animal, is now well known in Europe, particularly in England where it was introduced and has become a nuisance. Without the native predators to control their number, as there are in America, gray squirrels in England have multiplied very rapidly and do considerable damage to crops and trees. Squirrel damage to an ear of corn can be readily shown because the squirrel will eat only the germ end of the corn kernel, leaving the large starch portion of the grain lying about. Although the gray squirrel lives in trees, it spends about half its time on the ground searching for food. The gray squirrel also does some good, however, because many of the nuts which it gathers and buries to be stored for food, it forgets about. Every nut forgotten is a tree planted.

Knotholes in trees make ideal nesting sites for the gray squirrel, but as the tree is continually growing and trying to seal up the hole, the squirrel must cut back the new growth and keep enlarging the hole with its teeth. In warm weather the gray squirrel will make a summer nest of leaves high in the fork of some branch. These nests average about eighteen inches in diameter and are particularly conspicuous in the winter when all the other leaves have fallen. Discarded nut shells which have been opened by the squirrel and bear its tooth marks are also good squirrel signs.

The American red squirrel has the habit of sitting in certain spots to feed and allowing the discarded nuts and cones to fall in a large, easily seen trash pile known as a midden heap. In fact it shreds cones, and is partial to pine and spruce forest.

In walking about, squirrels use their legs alternately, as do most animals. When in a hurry they bound, so that the prints of their hind feet are placed in front of the prints made by their front feet. As their front feet are always placed side by side, this gives the tracks the appearance of sets of exclamation points.

Rabbits and Hares

RABBITS AND HARES have been introduced to lands in which they were not formerly found and are now established almost everywhere in the world. Some of these introductions, as in Australia, have had devastating effects. Where there were no natural predators to limit their numbers, the rabbits multiplied by the millions and ravaged the countryside of all vegetation. Rabbits and hares were at one time classified as rodents but now are placed in a separate order because they have four incisors in the tops of their mouths, whereas the rodents have only two. If you should find a skull, small secondary incisors located behind the main upper pair will identify it as that of a rabbit or a hare.

It is very hard to see the actual toe marks in rabbits' tracks because so much hair grows on their foot pads. The placement of their feet leaves a pattern which is easily recognized, as mentioned previously. When they hop slowly, their tracks may be three to five feet apart, but when they are frightened rabbits make bounds of fifteen feet and hares can cover more than twenty feet at a single leap.

In addition to tracks, rabbits and hares leave many other signs such as their small, marble-shaped droppings and their sharp, diagonal cuts on vegetation. These animals will often gnaw the bark off trees and if such gnawing is done completely around the tree, girdling it, the tree

(bottom left)
A **mouse's tracks** are among the neatest in nature. They form a dainty lacelike pattern, at times intertwined with the tail marks.

(bottom right)
Rat tracks are more often seen in flour or in waterfront mud. Because rats carry disease, they are frequently threatened with extermination. To escape danger they live in elaborate underground tunnels to which they can quickly run.

(below)
Originally from Central Asia, the **house mouse** has spread wherever man has gone. It is omnivorous but prefers cereals and stored foods.

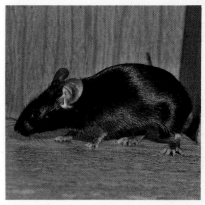

The **snowshoe rabbit** derives its name from the stiff hairs that grow on the sides of its feet each winter. These are effective as snowshoes and allow the animal to travel even in heavy snow. In summer this adaptable hare is brown; in winter the coat turns white, dark only at the ear tips.

will die. However very often rabbits get the blame for this damage when the real culprit is the meadow mouse, which also girdles trees. If we examine the girdling carefully, we can determine from the size of the tooth marks whether it was done by a mouse or a rabbit.

The American cottontails and hares, with the exception of one species in the state of Idaho, do not dig burrows to live in, although some of them may frequent burrows dug by other animals. The European rabbit, however, does dig extensive tunnels and interlocking subterranean systems called warrens, which may cover acres of land and are prominent features of the land.

Although the snowshoe rabbit, or varying hare, of North America has two names, both of which are descriptive, it is really a hare. It is called a snowshoe rabbit because in autumn long stiff guard hairs grow out from the sides of its feet. When the toes are spread apart these long hairs double the area covered and form effective "snowshoes" which allow the animal to walk over soft snow without sinking in. It is also called varying hare because it changes hue twice a year. In the autumn it molts its brown hair and replaces it with white hair. This winter coat is excellent camouflage and makes it very hard to see the hare when it is sitting on snow. The spring molt sheds the white hair and replaces it with brown, which allows the hare to blend in with its dark forest surroundings. The arctic hare is also white, except for black tips to its ears, but it is white all year long.

Bears—Brown, Black and Grizzly

THE BEARS ARE the largest meat-eating land animals in the world. Debate still rages over which of the bears is the largest, the polar bear or the Alaskan brown bear, although most experts believe it is the latter. The polar bear is circumpolar in range and spends most of its life on the frozen sea, where it hunts for seals and walruses which are its main food. Tracks of the polar bear are very indistinct because there is so much hair on the soles of their feet that practically no pads show.

The brown bear is now found mainly in Alaska, but at one time it also inhabited Europe. The brown bear and the grizzly bear are now being treated as the same species. Their large plantigrade tracks may measure sixteen inches long and ten inches wide. Surely a track like this, once seen, can never be forgotten nor confused with anything else. The toes on the forefeet are long, strong and sharply curved. Because of their weight and their long claws, these bears cannot climb trees. In areas where they are unmolested, these bears will follow trails which have become deep-rutted through use by generations of their ancestors. Their tracks are also seen along sea beaches and river edges where the bears go to catch fish. Grasses, tuberous plants and berries are also eaten. Bears frequently tear apart rotten logs to get at the termites and ants which live in them. They also overturn stones in their search for insects. Bears will dig out any of the ground-nesting squirrels that they can locate.

Often bears will shred the bark from spruce, fir and pine trees in order to eat the soft pulp beneath. In addition, they frequently mark trees in other manners. Having such long hair makes them a haven for fleas and other biting insects. To get relief, bears will stand up against a tree and rub their backs against the rough bark. Sometimes they will mark a tree as a sign claiming their territory. They stand on the ground and rub themselves against the tree, leaving their scent, and they also tear off the bark as high as they can reach. Other bears supposedly can then come along to see just how they measure up.

(left)
Bears like the soft pulp beneath the bark of some trees, and so their marks are often seen on tree trunks along forest trails. Other signs are tufts of hair on the bark where they have rubbed their backs to get rid of insects. The long-clawed specimen in this photograph is a **grizzly bear** from Yellowstone National Park.

(bottom left)
Unlike the brown bear, **black bears** can climb trees, and in doing so they cut marks into the bark. Extremely adaptable, they sometimes live near developed areas, where their presence is often unsuspected.

(bottom right)
One of the most noticeable things about a **bear's track** is its size, which may measure 16 inches long and 10 inches wide. The tracks are usually very clear because they are placed separately, not one over the other.

Black bears climb trees frequently and can do it so fast that they actually seem to gallop up. In climbing smooth-barked trees, the bears' claws will cut scratches into the bark which become permanent scars.

The brown, grizzly and black bears are omnivorous and will eat any type of food that they can find or catch. Because of this, their dung is often of different composition. When feeding on meat it will be compacted and segmented. When they feed upon vegetation the dung will be a shapeless mass much like that of a cow.

With the coming of cold weather these three kinds of bears gorge themselves and get very fat. They then stop eating and seek out some sheltered spot in which to pass the winter. They are not true hibernators, however, because their body temperatures remain almost normal and, although they become lethargic, they do not become torpid. If disturbed they can be easily roused and they may come out of their dens at any time. The females usually give birth to their young during this period.

The spectacled bears of South America are almost entirely vegetarians, while the sloth bears of India feed mainly upon insects. The Malayan sun bear is the smallest of the bears and one of the most intelligent. One striking thing about the sun bear's tracks is that each foot is turned inward as the bear walks.

The Cat Family

SOME MEMBERS of the cat family are among the largest and the strongest of the meat-eating animals; they are certainly some of the most ferocious. The large cats are found on most of the large land masses of the world: the puma in North America, the jaguar in Central and South America and the tiger, lion and leopard in Africa and Asia. Lions once inhabited Europe, too, but were exterminated in the time of the Romans.

These cats are almost strictly meat-eaters, very seldom eating anything else. Most of them prefer to make their own kills and will not eat carrion. Their habits are the same in that they usually carefully stalk their prey, then make a short dash, spring upon it and bear it to the ground. Or they may select some secluded spot high in the trees and wait until their prey happens to pass beneath them, when they drop down and kill it. Among the lions the females usually do the killing, although it is the male who eats first. Lions usually travel in large family groups called "prides", while most of the other large cats are solitary or travel in pairs.

After making a kill, the leopard carries its victim's body high up into a tree where it will be safe and where the leopard can feed on it at its leisure. Lions usually eat what they want of a kill and leave the rest to be devoured by vultures, jackals and hyenas. The puma will eat its fill and then cover what is left of its prey with sticks and vegetation.

The **bobcat** is more adaptable than its counterpart, the Canadian lynx. It is smaller, requires less range and can survive on smaller prey.

Lions (above) once ranged over Europe, but they are found today only in Asia and Africa south of the Sahara. They live in groups known as "prides," the number varying between ten and twenty, and cooperate both in hunting and in defending themselves. After making a kill they generally eat their fill and leave the rest to scavengers. On the other hand the **puma** (below) covers the remains of its kill and returns to finish its meal at a later time. Native to North America, the puma resembles a small lioness and has similar, uniform color. As with other large, wild animals, lions and pumas have been driven to the point of extinction in many places by excessive hunting, the clearing of land and the disappearance of the animals on which they prey. The **track of an African lion** (right) may be taken as typical of the cat family, showing just four toes.

Nature has equipped the **lynx** with large, oversized feet so that it can travel over soft snow without sinking in. The hind feet overlap or are placed in the front track.

When it is hungry again, the puma returns to the kill as long as it remains fresh, until it has eaten all of it.

The tracks of all these animals are similar, with each foot track showing just four toes. The snow leopard of Tibet has more hair on its feet than the other big cats because this is a mountain animal which lives right up to the snow line. Dung of the cat family is seldom seen because they all cover their dung. The scratched-up heaps of dirt, however, are just as effective for identifying the cats as would be the dung itself. The cats will sometimes scratch claw marks on smooth-barked trees in an effort to sharpen their claws by removing the dead, excess nail growth.

One large cat which is quite different from the rest is the cheetah or hunting leopard of Asia and Africa. Although of the cat family, the cheetah has a dog-like head, round pupils instead of the vertical ellipses of other cats, dog-like feet, and partially retractable claws. Cheetahs are the swiftest of the mammals and have been clocked at seventy miles per hour. They have a gentle disposition and have long been tamed by man to be used as hunting animals. In the wild, the cheetah will stalk its prey and actually run it down and kill it. Even the swiftest gazelles are easily taken by this animal.

The lynx of Canada and the lynx of Europe and Siberia are the

same animal, although they had formerly been thought to be two different species. Since lynx dwell in areas where there is heavy snowfall, their bodies have been modified for this purpose. They have a dense coat of hair, long, strong legs and oversized feet. These large feet have long, stiff hairs growing on them and when the toes are spread, the lynx can walk over soft snow which would bog down such animals as a fox or coyote. Their tracks are large and round and could easily be taken for the tracks of a much larger animal. Lynx weigh between twenty-five and forty pounds. Their main food is the snowshoe rabbit, which is a cyclic animal whose numbers reach a high peak of density and then crash to a low survival population. So closely is the lynx tied to the snowshoe's cycle that its numbers follow up and down accordingly, although the lynx's cycle usually lags one year behind that of the snowshoe.

The bobcat looks very much like the lynx and sometimes grows almost as large. The bobcat, however, lacks the long-haired ear tufts of the lynx. It is more adaptable, too, and may be found in the cold snow belt, in mountainous regions, in deep swamps or in dry deserts. Living under such varied conditions, the bobcat eats a much more varied diet and does not suffer the cyclic population crashes of the lynx.

There are many smaller members of the wild cat family which look

A member of the dog family, the **wolf** uses its tail to communicate with other wolves. For instance, when the tail is drooping and held between the hind legs, it may indicate submission to a dominant wolf. Because wolves are steadily decreasing in number and in range, it is rare to come across their tracks. The outline of the track is angular like that of a coyote and the front print may be larger than the hind one.

(above, left)

The **dingo** is believed to be descended from domestic dogs brought to Australia long ago. When they began to prey on sheep, professional "dog-hunters" all but eliminated them from remote areas.

(above, right)

Fastest member of the dog family, the **coyote** is one of the few animals that seems to be on the increase. It lives in underground dens that can easily be identified by size, leftover food scraps and bits of coyote hair.

just like someone's lost kittens. Some of them are the direct ancestors of our many domesticated cats of today. People who own cats know that they do not really own them in the same manner that a dog is owned. Most cats can, and often do, easily revert to the wild state.

Members of the Dog Family

SOME OF THE BEST tracking opportunities may come from following the tracks of a pet cat or dog. They have retained enough of their wild habits to be most interesting. A dog, for example, will probably run along until it comes to a scent post such as a tree or fire hydrant, upon which it will deposit urine. This habit is followed by all members of the dog family from the wolf right down to the smallest fox. It is also interesting to note that the fifth toe up on the inside of the front legs of members of the dog family never shows in their tracks.

The wolves, the largest members of the dog family, are steadily being pushed back to a smaller range by the advance of civilization. Once common in Europe, they are now practically exterminated there. The buffalo wolf of the United States has been exterminated and the gray wolf is found in just a few pockets of land in the northern states, although it still ranges widely in Canada. The red wolf is still holding on to a small range in the south-central portion of the United States. The timber wolf of Canada has been steadily pushed back as more of the forested areas are felled by the pulp-cutters.

Where once the howl of wolf music gave one a thrill, the silence of the night now is broken only by the call of lesser creatures. An occasional wolf track can still be seen along the beaches and in the mud on the portage trails, serving as a reminder that this is wolf country. Some of the tracks measure over four inches in length and width. A wolf which makes such tracks will weigh 125 pounds or more. Wolves' dung is usually composed of masses of hair and sometimes small mammal

Coyotes resemble wolves. Normally they are found alone or in pairs and may do their hunting in relays. Their food is largely rodents and carrion, and seldom domestic stock. In the southwestern United States, antirodent poison has killed off large numbers of coyotes, thus defeating the farmers' original purpose by reducing the natural check on the rodent population.

bones. Many people do not know that wolves will actually hunt for mice and small rodents as well as for big-game animals. Wolves hunt in family groups and need the strength of numbers to tear down an animal the size of a moose or a caribou.

The population is finally learning something that the Eskimo and the Indians have known all along: when wolves prey upon larger game they actually improve the herds. Invariably the animal the wolves select is not as healthy a specimen as the rest of the herd or it would not have fallen behind when the wolves charged them. If all the herd keeps the same pace, the wolves will leave and seek out another herd until they find a prey animal which falls behind and can be cut down.

The coyote is the fastest member of the dog family and can run at speeds of up to forty-five miles per hour. As strange as it may seem, the coyote is actually increasing in numbers and extending its range. Formerly found only in the prairies of the western United States, the coyote has gone north to Alaska and to the upper portions of Canada, and has spread eastward to the New England states. It had never occupied this range before. The abandonment of many of the poor backcountry farms in the eastern United States created an area to the liking of the coyote. Some actually migrated east while others have been pets which have escaped or been released. Both coyotes and wolves will dig their own underground dens. These are usually in sandy slopes or river banks to make the digging easier. They can readily be identified by the large size of the hole, the remnants of food particles, such as pieces of fur and bits of bone, and by the animal's hair itself which may be caught on a projecting root.

The dingo of Australia is an animal which has been extending its range. Originally Australia, like most of the other oceanic islands, did not have any members of the dog family present. When the first primitive people came to Australia, they brought their wild dogs with them. The dingo simply reverted to the wild and became established.

Although mainly nocturnal, **red foxes** will sunbathe or sleep in the open in good weather. They are solitary except in the breeding season. **Fox tracks** show claw marks, which distinguish them from those of a cat.

Arctic foxes are often bred because of the value of their pelts. Their usual habitat is along the northern seacoasts, where they feed on birds and small rodents.

Following the Fox

THE EUROPEAN RED FOX appears identical to the red fox of North America. The gray fox was native to the United States but the colonists found that they could not hunt it with hounds and horses because the gray fox does not like to run. It inhabits dense areas of swamps, thickets or rocky ledges. If pursued it will crawl down a hole or climb up a tree. It is the only member of the dog family which climbs readily. Rather than give up their sport, the colonists imported the red fox from England in 1760 and released it on Long Island, in the lower part of New York State, and in New Jersey. From that beginning, the red fox is thought to have enlarged its range until it is now found in most parts of the United States. In moving northward the red fox readily bred with the red fox of Canada.

The red fox prefers open country, where it can see all around to watch for danger. It runs well and is very intelligent. It may do some harm by feeding on poultry, game birds and animals but it also does a great amount of good by helping to control rodents such as mice and rats.

Tracks of a large house cat, a red fox and a gray fox look similar but can easily be told apart. The cat track will show no claw marks, so that one can be eliminated. The gray fox has larger toe and foot pads than does the red fox; that is the key difference. The red fox has a large amount of hair between its toes, and just a small part of its pads show in the track. While the gray fox will den up, the red fox prefers to sleep right out in the snow and its beds can often be found. Both foxes use dens for their young but do not dig their own, preferring to enlarge the den of a woodchuck or use a natural cavity.

Following the track of a fox, particularly a red fox, after a newly fallen snow is a pleasurable and educational way to spend a winter's day. A tracker learns to respect the fox's hunting ability after seeing how thoroughly it searches every possible piece of cover which may contain prey animals or birds.

When the ground is not frozen, a fox will bury any surplus food that it catches but cannot eat. It will dig a small hole, place the meat inside, and then cover it, using its nose to replace the earth. When the wild cherries fall off the tree, the dung of both the red and the gray foxes will be composed almost entirely of them.

The arctic fox is found in the far north. This beautiful fox may be pure white in winter or pale blue, and brownish or dark bluish grey in summer. In winter the hairs which grow between the pads of its feet almost cover the pads completely. This not only provides good insulation but also gives the arctic fox a better grip when running on icy surfaces. Although usually found along the sea-coast, where it scavenges and feeds upon birds and their nests, as well as on small rodents, the arctic fox sometimes strays hundreds of miles south into the forests. In its tundra haunts there is no other animal its size with a similar track, so once again elimination would make its tracks easy to identify.

Raccoons, Skunks and Weasels

THE RACCOON IS strictly a New World animal and its tracks are very easy to identify. The track of the hind foot resembles a miniature bear's track or even the track of some long-toed human baby. Since raccoons feed along the water's edge, their tracks are usually in abundance there. Pincers and legs of crayfish will show where the raccoons have been successful in their hunting. When sweet or field corn is in the "milk", corn fields are places to look for the raccoon. If its tracks cannot be found, evidence of its having been there will still be plentiful. The raccoon gluts itself on the corn and is so greedy that it pulls down and destroys far more corn than it actually eats.

The toes on the raccoon's forefeet are long and nimble. It is amazing to see the things that a raccoon can do with its "fingers". If the raccoon had had an opposable thumb, it might have given man competition for control of the earth. The raccoon's dung is similar to that of a fox but much larger in diameter, for the raccoon grows to about twice the

Swift, agile and a good climber, the **weasel** hunts mainly by **scent.** When it captures its prey it is a relentless killer, often killing far more than needed for food.

weight of a fox. Most raccoons weigh about fifteen to eighteen pounds with some big ones going up to twenty-five pounds or more.

Raccoons will nest in rock ledges but prefer hollow trees. Any tree used as a den will be easy to identify, because the rough bark of the tree will be loaded with raccoon hair.

Skunks are often maligned and are not given the credit for all the good they do. It is true that occasionally one will kill poultry or take eggs, but on the whole skunks are good friends to a farmer. Insects form the bulk of the skunk's diet. One of the best signs of a skunk's activities is the small conical hole which it digs in search of beetles. Hundreds of these holes will dot every field where the skunk is working. Every small stone and dried piece of cow's dung will be turned over so that the insects hiding under there can be eaten. The skunk's own dung is composed almost entirely of the hard, bright indigestible pieces of beetle shells.

Tracks of the striped skunk show the whole foot very plainly. The **skunk** is well known for defending itself by spraying foul-smelling fluid from its anal glands. Less well known is its warning before this act: standing on its forefeet and raising its tail with the tip down and, finally, flipping the tip up.

Skunks are plantigrade, and the whole foot shows plainly in their tracks. The long claw marks are a very noticeable feature. Because of their odd rolling gait, the skunks' tracks are all one behind the other but on a diagonal line. The very pungent scent of their musk, used in defending themselves, is also an infallible sign of skunks.

The skunk is really a member of the weasel family but it has grown so fat and sluggish that it no longer resembles the rest of this lithe-bodied, agile family. While the Alaskan brown bear is the world's largest meat-eating animal, the least weasel is the smallest. This tiny mite weighs about two and a half ounces. Most members of this family look like snakes with legs; they are designed that way so that they can follow mice underground through their tunnels and kill them. They are an important check on small rodents. Weasels are exceedingly bloodthirsty, however, and will kill any creature they can overcome, even though their prey may be many times their own size. They often kill far in excess of their needs just for the pleasure of doing so. Often a single weasel will kill seventy-five chickens in a single night and just drink some of the blood. Seventy-five chickens would be enough food to last a weasel for a lifetime.

Weasels are very energetic and usually travel by bounding along. As the hind feet usually fall right where the front feet have been, their tracks are a long line of matched dots. When such tracks lead into every hole, brush heap and rock pile in the area they lead the tracker on the trail of a hunting weasel.

(above, left)
Flying foxes are tree-dwelling fruit bats. During the day they hang upside down in trees, and at night they go on feeding expeditions, foraging for mango, guava and other fruit.

(above, right)
Opossum tracks are very unusual, for they resemble human hands more than animal paws. This is mainly because the animal has a large thumb.

Aquatic Meat-eaters

ALTHOUGH THERE ARE many other types of meat-eaters in the world, some are aquatic by nature. These are the seals, sea lions and walruses. The sea lions are perhaps the best known because they are the ones which perform at the circus, billed as "trained seals". These animals never stray far from water because their limbs have been adapted to be used as flippers in swimming. They also need a water medium to help support their large body weight. Some of them clamber up on the sea beaches just for the breeding and calving seasons, spending the rest of the year at sea.

Bats—Creatures of Flight

THE WATER MAMMALS are not the only ones to live in a different medium. The bats' forearms and hands have become modified into wings so that flight is possible. Flying squirrels and some phalangers glide, but only the bats are capable of free, flapping flight. Although they are good flyers, bats are extremely awkward on the ground. A bat's feet are directed backward so that it can hang upside down but the bat is not able to bend them forward for walking. When on the ground, the bat moves forward by pulling itself along with its wings and pushing with its feet. If the ground is dusty, the wing scrapes as well as the foot marks will show in the tracks. The most common sign of bats is their dung, although it is often confused with or mistaken for that of a mouse. That is a good comparison, however, because a bat does look like a "flying mouse". In some caves bat dung or "guano" becomes so deep that it is gathered and sold for fertilizer, since it is very high in nitrogen content. Many of the bats, such as the free-tail bats, eat only insects while others eat fruit or drink the nectar from flowers or, as in the case of vampires, drink blood. One bat is a fisherman.

The Burrowing Mole

THE MOLES are specialized for their life underground, with legs which are shortened and strengthened for digging. Their forefeet are enlarged into shovel-like appendages. In soft earth a mole can literally swim through the soil and disappear. The fur on most moles is different from that of other animals in that it will lie down in any direction. Because they spend so much time underground, moles' eyes and ears are very small. The tracks of a mole are not often seen, but his tunnels and burrowings just under the surface of the earth are known to all.

The Armadillo

THE ARMADILLOS belong to a group known as *Edentata* which also includes the sloths and anteaters; they are found only in the New World. The nine-banded armadillo is found in the most southern states of the United States. Armadillos feed primarily upon insects, particularly ants, but will also occasionally eat the eggs of ground-nesting birds and some snakes. They have four toes on the front foot and five toes on the hind foot. Each toe is equipped with a strong, stout nail to be used by this animal in securing its food and in digging its burrows, which are about eight inches in diameter. The armadillo is covered with scaly plates like the armour of a medieval knight. When frightened the armadillo scampers for the safety of its burrow; if it cannot reach that, it will curl up like a ball, hoping that its shell will provide the needed protection. The scaly tail leaves drag marks in the track. Because the armadillo's main food is the ants which it digs up, it also consumes a lot of earth in the process. This causes its dung to look like elongated clay marbles.

The Opossums

THE OPOSSUMS belong to the order known as *Marsupialia*, meaning pouched animals, which contains some of the most weird and di-

(above)
Usually gregarious, **free-tailed bats** roost in flocks that number in the millions. This family of bats has broad ears, united at the base; half of the tail is free of the body. Sometimes wing marks can be seen on dusty trails, along with foot marks.

(bottom, far left)
The **armadillo** is well protected by shields. Some armadillos are able to burrow, and their holes can be seen throughout the southwestern United States.

(left)
Like all possums, this mouse-sized **Australian honey possum** carries its young in a pouch. It feeds on leaves, fruits and flowers.

verse creatures. Some of the marsupials live underground, some live in water, some glide through the air, while others, such as the kangaroos, have tremendous jumping ability. Different species are found throughout the world but by far most of the specimens are found in Australia.

The little honey possum of south-western Australia looks like a long-tailed mouse. This possum is about three inches long, has an elongated snout and a very long tongue which is used for probing flowers to get at the pollen and nectar for food. Insects found in the flowers are also eaten or insects may be chased, caught and eaten. The long whip-like tail is prehensile and can be used in climbing. This is of great help since the honey possum spends most of its time in trees and vines. Both the front and the hind feet show only four toes, although five are present. At some time in the distant past the second and third toes became fused into one unit but this single toe still has two toenails.

The Virginia opossum inhabits the United States and is constantly expanding its range. "Playing possum", whereby this animal feigns death, is still the subject of much discussion, because it has not been proved whether the animal controls this action or not. Opossum tracks cannot be confused with those of any other American animal because the hind foot of the opossum has an opposable thumb and looks just like a human hand. The large thumb has no toenail.

Tracks and trails are all around us in the outdoors. Reading tracks and sign may never be more than just a pleasurable pastime, but it serves to make us feel at home afield. In addition, the practice of observation developed through tracking broadens our horizons and enriches our lives.

This **Malayan rat** lives in jungle trees. It has a powerful head and prominent orange incisors, which can cause considerable damage to plants.

BIRDS

N O GROUP OF ANIMALS can delight us, capture our imagination, expand our awareness and reflect our moods and feelings better than the birds. Some people seek them out in their favored haunts, and others are merely conscious of them while going about their own daily activities. Yet for all of us there are those rare, unplanned moments when the sight or sound of birds has held some deep, and perhaps hidden, significance.

These winged, feathered creatures are often useful to man. They eat harmful insects, help control the populations of vermin and clear away refuse and carcasses. Some species are regularly hunted or raised for food. It may well be, however, that we have taken them too much for granted. Many species of birds have disappeared from certain areas or become wholly extinct, and all over the world today others are endangered: by overhunting and senseless slaughter, pollution of the waters, drainage of the wetlands and the encroachment of man on once-secluded breeding areas. In some cases protective measures have helped, but the battle to save the birds is still far from won.

Birds are found over water and all types of terrain, in all climates and in densely populated cities as well as uninhabited regions. The chapters that follow describe and, when possible, illustrate their plumage; structural adaptations for predation or seed-eating and for flying, running, wading or swimming; diet and food-getting activities; courtship, nesting and breeding habits; habitat and distribution; migration; calls and songs; and any interesting peculiarities of particular families or species. Each of the five chapters focuses on a different category of birds.

Often common and popular birds, SONG BIRDS use their voices to communicate with each other and perhaps for the sheer joy of singing.

GAME BIRDS, hunted for food and sport, include the tastiest as well as some of the most colorful wild species.

Providing magnificent spectacles but, unfortunately, easy targets for some foolish hunters, BIRDS OF PREY are a natural check on the populations of many animals.

SEA BIRDS range over all the oceans of the earth and usually breed on the coasts or on remote islands.

Swamps, marshy grounds, deltas and the borders of streams, rivers, ponds and lakes are the homes of the many and varied BIRDS OF THE WETLANDS.

► *You can tell them apart as they communicate in characteristic sounds.*

Song Birds

WE ARE CLOSER TO BIRDS than to any other living creature in the sense that from early childhood we are made aware of their presence by their bright plumage, their vocal language and the fact that they allow us to intrude into every aspect of their lives.

Because of this, we are aware of bird song and it is not too long before we ask pertinent questions such as, "Why do they sing?"; or, "Do they enjoy singing?" To deal with the first question: song is an important biological function in that it is vital to the survival of the individual and the species. Song is a basic part of the ritual of staking territories, courtship, display and mating. Briefly, song indicates to the individual bird the location and boundary of a territory; the vigor and dominance of the bird; the stage the bird has reached in its sexual cycle and the location of the nest site.

The European robin will indicate its territory to another robin or a new rival in the district by its song. In other words, it is advertising its home, its plot of land and at the same time issuing a warning to other robins to keep away.

These are some of the biological functions of the song; but is that the whole function? For example, do birds enjoy singing as some people enjoy singing in the bath or in a choir? It is, of course, impossible for us to say because they cannot communicate to us what they are feeling. There are, however, many ornithologists who have come to the conclusion that bird song *is* an expression of joy or some similar emotion. In fact, it has even been suggested that bird song could be the beginning of true artistic creation and expression and that possibly birds

It is perhaps because of their singing that we are most aware of birds and are so delighted to have them around us. While bird songs may be expressions of joy, they also have important functions in the life of each individual and species. (top right) In spring, during courting and nesting time, **rose-breasted grosbeaks** are bursting with song. They are also allies of a sort, since they eat harmful insects, especially the potato bug. (top, far right) Many **shrikes** impale their prey on thorns, creating a food store where they can return to when necessary. They prey on beetles, small birds and rodents. Some have attractive, musical voices.

(below)
Welcome heralds of spring, **bluebirds** nest in tree cavities, deserted woodpecker holes and—when provided —nest boxes. They will sometimes raise three broods in a season. Like other members of the thrush family, they are fine musicians.

(bottom)
The voice of a **magpie**, though not as pleasing as the song of a thrush or nightingale, is used for the same purposes as that of any song bird: communicating information, expressing emotion and establishing territorial rights.

are the evolutionary pioneers in the development of art. And could not primitive man have discovered rhythm and musical patterns from the song birds around him? It is a nice thought and an intriguing question.

Bird Language

WE SHOULD NOT, of course, separate song as something apart; it has to be regarded as only a portion of a bird's language. Neither should we consider those birds which produce pleasing melodies as unique. We may not find the voices of magpies, crows, jays or eagles as pleasing as that of the hermit thrush or nightingale, but they do have the same purpose. The voice is most certainly one of the most important methods of communication. As Dr. Maurice Burton has so aptly pointed out, because birds move about over such wide areas they have a greater need than most animals for vocal communication. The same principle can be applied to those people living in mountainous areas who communicate across considerable distances by special whistling or yodeling.

Birds frequently use their voices as a warning against approaching predators. The chaffinch will issue a warning call on sighting a hawk and a quite different call when the danger is over. The warning call is sufficient for other chaffinches and birds to make for the nearest bush or cover or to crouch low if they are on open ground. The alarm or fear call is not only recognizable to the same species but also to other species. The danger call of the blackbird, jay or titmouse is recognized as such by the song thrush, the nuthatch and other birds, and vice versa. Waders will respond to the warning calls made by herring gulls and arctic terns. A titmouse on the edge of a wood which is a chorus of bird song notices an approaching hawk; the titmouse calls, and the wood falls silent. The hawk passes over and disappears; the chaffinch calls that the danger has gone, and the wood fills with song again. Birds learn by association the significance of another species' call-note.

The voice is also used to communicate to others the location of food. Herring gulls have a special call when they have found a food supply and this brings other herring gulls to the source. There is an interesting case of two species of honey-guides inhabiting the tropical forests and woodlands of Africa. Both species have a taste for beeswax but, as they are insect eaters and not dependent on the wax, they do not have the kind of bills needed for breaking into the nest. They have therefore developed an interesting association with the ratel or honey-badger and the African native. Both the ratel and the African native have learned that when the honey-guide starts using his churring call, fans his tail and generally makes himself conspicuous, he has found a bees' nest and wants them to follow. After the native or ratel has robbed the nest, the honey-guide feeds on the broken honeycombs.

(above)
A true social parasite, the **common cuckoo** lays its
eggs in the nests of other birds, one egg to a nest.
At the same time it removes one of the host's eggs.
The young nestling, which is brought up by the
foster parents, grows quickly and often pushes the
other young birds out of the nest. If it hatches first
it may simply push the eggs out. Other species,
however, such as the yellow-billed and black-billed
cuckoos of North America and the roadrunners,
build their own nests and are not parasites.

(right)
Probably the best known of the large North
American sparrow family is the **song sparrow,** which
has a varied musical song. This bird likes to sing from
a prominent perch, such as a fence post or the top
of a bush.

Birds will use their voices as another means of contact. During migration flight, they will call to keep the flock together. Distressed or hungry young birds make effective use of the voice to communicate their plight to their parents.

In summing up, it is interesting to note that song and bird language is very much a part of need to survive, to claim territory and maintain contact with the flock; it is vitally associated with the creatures' sexual drive and, when used to give warning of predators, of their "social relationships". One might wonder if bird song could have fear or apprehension as its basis.

The Thrush Family

THE THRUSH FAMILY has some of the finest musicians. It is, therefore, appropriate in a book about song birds that we devote some attention to them. The family is a large one, and includes all the familiar true thrushes—the blackbird, song thrush, American robin,

A **young song thrush** (right) must break out of its shell without help from its parents. In doing so it is aided by a special tool, the "egg tooth" on the upper beak. This little tooth, having served its only purpose, disappears soon after hatching. Like most song birds, a **mature thrush** (below) continues singing until sunset or later. Songs apparently serve primarily to warn other birds away from the singer's territory.

ring ousel, redwing and fieldfare. Around this main group, we have the chatlike birds, such as the rock thrushes of Africa and Eurasia and the whistling thrush of South-eastern Asia. We also have in Europe the nightingales in this family, as well as redstarts, the chats and the famous European robin and the many forest robins of Africa. The thrush family, it can be seen, is a world-wide one.

Blackbirds and Song Thrushes

THE BLACKBIRD SHARES with the chaffinch the distinction of being the commonest bird in England and Wales, where, it has been estimated, there are ten million of each. It would not be an exaggeration to say it is a successful species with a wide distribution stretching as far north as Norway and south to Portugal, and with Russia well within its range. The blackbird also likes a wide variety of habitats, such as gardens, woods, copses, farmlands, swamp, plains and even coastal regions.

A small, short-tailed thrush with an upright posture, the **whinchat** (left) likes to perch conspicuously on the tops of bushes and plants. When courting the hen, the cock bird droops and quivers his wings, with head thrown back so that he displays his breast and white wing and tail feathers. Another member of the thrush family, the **European blackbird** (below) is common all over Europe, where it is both a resident and partially migratory. Its song is usually heard from February until after July.

(top left)
When disturbed a **blackbird** will give out a hysterical alarm note that alerts all other birds in the neighborhood. Its proper song, however, is clear, rich and soft. Blackbirds prefer low places for their nests, which are usually built by the female. Her eggs are bluish green and have red-brown speckles.

(top right)
The large white crescent on its breast distinguishes the **ring ouzel,** a member of the thrush family, which prefers the mountain regions of Central and Southern Europe. It builds a low nest and usually has two broods, one early and the other late in the spring.

(below)
Red-winged blackbirds are some of the first migrants of spring to arrive in North America. Their nests are usually built in swamps and marshy areas.

The song period of the blackbird is more restricted than that of the song thrush; normally it does not start until February and finishes after July. One of the first calls one hears from this bird is its panicky, almost hysterical, alarm note. Disturb a blackbird and it will warn every other bird of your approach. In contrast to this, its proper song is clear and fluent, and of a richer and softer tone than that of the thrush.

There is no difficulty in identifying the male blackbird with his glossy black plumage, orange bill and yellow eye rim. The female, on the other hand, is a subdued creature; just a rich sepia above, and a somewhat lighter brown below.

Blackbirds usually nest just a few feet from the ground in hedges, bushes and evergreens. Occasionally they will nest on the ground, sometimes high in trees and even in sheds. The nest is generally built by the female which starts late in March, or more often in April. She makes it of grasses and moss, held together and lined with mud, with an inner layer of grass. She lays three to five eggs which are bluish green, speckled with red-brown.

The main food of blackbirds is vegetable matter and insects and with more than a taste for fruit, they can do considerable damage in an orchard.

The song thrush is found throughout Europe, and even as far east as Siberia. In Britain it is one of the most liked of the common birds because it is found in familiar places such as gardens, shrubberies, woods, copses and meadows. The plumage is warm brown above with a buffish breast and small, narrow spots.

The food of the song thrush consists almost exclusively of earthworms and insects but it does have an appetite for snails. One will often come across a thrush's anvil (a stone which it uses to smash snail shells) littered with the remains of its last meal.

The song is loud and vigorous but rather repetitive, and has been

best described by B. W. Tucker as "a succession of simple but musical phrases, distinguished by their repetitive characters, great variety and clear enunciation". The song thrush sings most of the year and can mimic other birds.

American and British Robins

THE AMERICAN ROBIN is quite a different bird from the European robin. Its Old World counterpart is the blackbird. It is a big, bouncy bird—easy to recognize by its grey back, black head and bright brick-red breast. The song which heralds the spring equinox is a clear whistling chorus, sustained with short phrases of two or three notes.

The fact that the American robin is so widely distributed and has a fondness for being near human habitation, probably makes it the best-known bird in the United States. Robins are to be found in wooded areas and marshy woods, as well as in parks and on lawns

Thrushes are popular and common song birds found in parks, gardens, woods and meadows as well as mountainous areas. Their diet is mainly insects and earthworms, but they will also eat snails, smashing them against rocks, and wild fruits and berries in winter. Some species have spotted undersides, such as the wood thrush and hermit thrush, both North American species, and the European song thrush. The song thrush sings most of the year and can mimic other birds. It is found as far east as Siberia, where the Siberian blue robin, another member of this group, also lives. The smallest European thrush is the redwing.

What is most unusual about the brief song of the **chaffinch** is that it tends to vary from country to country and even from one small area to another. Chaffinches live in couples and, when courting, the more attractively marked male may be seen chasing the hen in a quick, swerving flight.

(below)
Darting from a hedge or a perch, the **European robin** will seize an insect or a worm and then quickly dart back to the hedge again. This plucky bird, which differs considerably from the American robin, has an olive-brown back and a bright orange forehead, throat and breast.

(above)
A fondness for human society characterizes the **American robin,** a big, bouncy bird with a grey back and a brick-red breast. In some areas where insecticides have been heavily used, whole populations of robins have disappeared.

and around suburban homes. In fact projecting house ledges, gateway trestles and all kinds of bushes and tree forks provide acceptable sites for their substantial nests. The nest is made of mud reinforced with leaves and twigs, woven with leaves, twine, paper etc. Their nests can often be found around barns, sheds and other out-buildings. They will normally contain four or five greenish blue eggs.

The robin, like many other song birds, has suffered heavily from the indiscriminate use of insecticides. Studies made by Dr. George Wallace provided some frightening facts. For example, tests made on sixty-nine robins showed that all of them had DDT in their tissues or organs, and of another ninety robins analyzed, the brains contained levels of DDT comparable to levels found in those dying of experimental DDT poisoning. One cannot get away from the fact that the disappearance of whole populations of robins from certain areas is the direct result of insecticides. This is only one species on the American continent; but we know (though too few are aware) that wildlife in many parts of the world is being carelessly and selfishly destroyed by the use of these agents.

It is a curious fact that the resident robins in Britain are different in their habits from the ones on the continent of Europe. The latter race is secretive and skulking in its actions, while it would not be an exaggeration to say that the British robin has absolute trust in man. They will often enter a house for food, perch on a garden spade ready to pounce on insects as they are disturbed by it, and will nest in garden sheds and garages. Little wonder that the British ornithologists have adopted the robin as their national bird.

Territorial possessiveness is a strongly marked characteristic of the robin, it being quite aggressive to its own kind and, for that matter, to other birds as well. Robins usually establish their territories in August until late December (when they pair up) and the females will often have separate territories from their mates.

The breeding season usually commences in early April, although breeding has been known to occur in winter, and the hen builds the nest alone, with dead leaves and moss, softly lined with hair and feathers. The nest is cleverly concealed, and often robins have been known to make use of old tin cans and kettles as a nesting site. A good way to encourage these birds to nest in your garden is to provide them with such containers. Robins have olive-brown backs, with bright orange foreheads, throats and breasts bordered by pale grey and blue. Their food is mainly insects, spiders, centipedes and earthworms.

The Hermit Thrush and the Nightingale

THE HERMIT THRUSH is a brown-backed bird with a spotted breast, but for quick identification, look for the reddish tail which is conspicuous as the bird flies away. It is one of the finest American song birds, with clear flutelike notes quietly followed by half a dozen or more short, thinner ones which follow one another so rapidly as to produce an astonishing tremolo effect. The cadences spiral upwards and ascend higher and higher until the final one is beyond the range of most human ears; then follows a minute or so of silence, after which the whole rendering is repeated. This songster frequently continues its performance, at intervals, from shortly after sunset until the undercover of the woods is almost completely dark.

In spring and summer, the hermit thrush feeds mostly on insects,

Common all over Europe, the **robin "redbreast"** is easily identified by its rich orange breast. This species feeds on earthworms and small invertebrates; it is frequently trusting and even jaunty in man's company.

(above)
A shy bird easily concealed in thick underbrush, the **nightingale** would frequently go unnoticed were it not for its unmistakable song.

(below, left)
The best singer of all is probably this small **eastern nightingale.** Its nest is built of leaves, grasses and hair in the bushes, fairly close to the ground. Insects make up most of its diet.

(below, right)
By night, when other birds are quiet, as well as by day, this **great nightingale** sings its rich and varied song, made famous by poets and storytellers.

but in the winter it takes various wild fruits and berries. The nest, which is bulky, is usually built on the ground or close to it, and is made of grass, roots, leaves, dried moss. There are usually three or four pale greenish blue eggs.

Roger Tory Peterson tells a charming story of a hermit thrush which, weary of picking its way through the bewildering canyons of New York City, descended to Madison Avenue where, attracted by the palms, plants and flower displays of a florist shop, it flew in through the open transom and took refuge. Throughout the winter, the thrush led a comfortable existence, becoming extremely tame, even taking food from the hand. However, the following spring it became restless and one day departed. Two years later, during the autumn, a hermit thrush appeared in front of the same shop. The bird allowed itself to be picked up and the proprietors insisted it was the same bird. And why not? We do know that birds will often return to the same spot each winter.

Is there a more famous song bird than the nightingale? I do not think so. That is not to say the nightingale has the most beautiful song; indeed, many naturalists feel that it is not the beauty but the vigor and strength of its voice that is so impressive. One cannot get away from the fact that the nightingale has captivated more writers, poets and naturalists with its voice than any other song bird; T. A. Coward put it another way when he said: "No bird has had more rubbishy sentiment lavished upon it than the nightingale". The reason for its popularity is more probably due to its habit of singing at night when other song birds are normally silent, but it sings quite freely in the daytime, too. The song is rich and varied and the most exciting part is the deep bubbling "chooc-chooc-chooc-chooc", followed by the slower "pui, pui, pui" note which develops into a superb crescendo.

You are more likely to hear the nightingale than to see it because it tends to skulk in the cover provided by thick undergrowth. On seeing

This **song thrush** is a common bird in Europe, where it is sometimes called the "nightingale of the north." Its song, consisting of short, varied musical phrases, is loud and vigorous.

it, you will observe a russet brown bird with an even more russet tail. The nightingale is sturdy in build, and moves alertly with its tail cocked. In other words, you would be observing a larger, all brown European robin.

The breeding distribution of the nightingale in Britain is confined to certain parts of England and Wales, and is altogether absent from Scotland and Ireland. On the European continent, the nightingale is chiefly found in the Mediterranean area and western Europe.

During the breeding season, it prefers open deciduous woods and copses with thick undergrowth. In this type of vegetation, the hen builds the nest fairly close to the ground. This is made of dry leaves, lined with dry grasses and some hair, and four or five eggs are normally laid. Nightingales feed almost exclusively on insects and animal matter.

(right)
Although shy and retiring, the **wood thrush** frequently nests near human habitation. It feeds on grasshoppers, crickets, caterpillars and a host of other insects.

(far right)
This species of **bulbul** is one of the commonest birds in Africa. A fruit-eater, it is sociable and likes the companionship of the flock.

(below)
The **meadowlark** is not really a lark but a member of the New World family which contains the bobolink, red-winged blackbirds and orioles. It is found in fields and meadows and often joins flocks of starlings.

Honey-eaters

THE TUI, unlike the wax-eye, is a true honey-eater. It belongs to a group of birds, confined almost exclusively to Australasia, which are mainly arboreal nectar- and fruit-eaters. The most interesting feature of the honey-eaters is the brush tongue which has been adapted to collect nectar. This is long and grooved, cleft in four parts delicately frayed to form the "brush" that licks up the nectar.

The honey-eater family has produced a diverse collection of birds, some resembling goldcrests, others warblers. Some look like sunbirds or hummingbirds and some are large and similar to orioles or magpies and there are even birds looking like tits, nuthatches and flycatchers. One is immediately struck by the fact that the Australian continent has produced a group of birds with variations that can be compared with the marsupials and the mammals.

Most of the honey-eaters are forest birds keeping to treetops and flowering trees, and only a few visit the ground. But as you can imagine, with such a diverse group of birds, the many species have varied habitats; some are found in swamps, some in mountainous areas, others in dune and plain country.

Although the honey-eaters belong to the Australian region, where they are well distributed and form a special bird group, there is one genus which has isolated itself from the rest. Its members are found in South Africa where they are called sugar birds. Honey-eaters are to be found in Hawaii, New Zealand, New Guinea and other islands in the region.

The tui is characteristic of the family, found in forests and plantations, but they will visit cities where they know there are nectar-bearing flowers. It is not being too anthropomorphic about the tui to describe them as behaving in a very extrovert fashion—noisy, aggressive, fast in movement, and of a restless nature. Their flight is audible when they are wing clapping, they are proficient acrobats and can often be seen twisting, falling and tumbling.

The best time to watch them is on a summer's day, when they are most active. You can often see them swinging upside down as they insert their long and protusible tongue into flowers for nectar. During cold periods they will also supplement their diet with insects and eat berries. Their many voices provide numerous musical phrases—plus jangling, gurgling and whistling calls.

The White-eyes

THE WHITE-EYES are a large and complex group of birds which includes more than eight species; in many ways their habits are similar to the honey-eaters' in that they have brush tongues and feed on insects, fruit and nectars and prefer to keep to trees. The white-eyes must have originated in Africa, where there are many species, but over very many years they have extended their range over the whole of Ethiopia, and the Oriental and Australasian regions. This is a remarkable achievement for such short-winged birds which are not long-distance migrants.

One good example of colonization by these birds is provided by the species called the wax-eye which must have crossed 1,200 miles of the Tasman Sea in the 1850s to set up home in New Zealand. It did this so successfully that the species is now flourishing there. In New Zealand, they enjoy a wide habitat (with the exception of the deep

A large thrush found throughout Europe and western Siberia, the **mistle thrush** gets its name from its habit of eating mistletoe berries. It can often be seen perching on tall trees and ringing out its song, which carries for a considerable distance.

Regardless of its form, any **bird's nest** serves mainly as a safe repository for the eggs. The nest itself, the eggs, or both, may be tinted and marked to blend with the surroundings.

forests), and in autumn and winter they flock together. It is this habit of keeping in flocks which has undoubtedly helped the white-eyes to establish themselves in new areas.

The wax-eye has a number of other names, including silver-eye, ring-eye and blight-bird. They received the last name when, much to the delight of orchard growers, they were seen attacking the insects which cause "woolly aphis" soon after their arrival in New Zealand; but, because they also attack buds and fruit, we have here one of those problem birds which cannot be easily classed either as beneficial or injurious to man. Recent studies of insectivorous birds rather suggest that it is the insects which control the number of birds. An abundance of insect food will usually result in a large clutch of eggs and, therefore, a larger number of young birds reared. A poor insect season will often have the reverse effect. But we must not forget that the wax-eye does tremendous good as a result of its fondness for nectar resulting in pollination of trees and shrubs.

Wax-eyes have a pleasant, rapid warbling song and breed during September to December, when they produce a clutch of three to four eggs. The nest is slightly built, cup-shaped and made of grass, lichen, spider's web, hair and moss, slung together hammock fashion between branches.

The Lyre-birds

THE LYRE-BIRDS of Australia and New Guinea are unique—not only in being found nowhere else but also in their extraordinary ability to mimic almost any sound they hear. There are two species:

the superb, and Albert's (so named after Queen Victoria's consort, Prince Albert). It is, however, the superb that has given the family its name. The lyre is formed by the beautifully curved outer pair of tail feathers which reach almost two feet in length. Although they have an individual song of their own, it is their ability to imitate the voices of other birds and animals which is so remarkable; indeed, they will imitate any sound they hear and include it in their own repertoire. Both the male and female mimic.

The breeding and nesting habits of the lyre-bird are also unusual. Not only does it nest in the winter, but the male establishes a territory, whose extent may be as much as half a mile, where he indicates several display grounds for carrying on his courtship activities. The female builds the nest unaided, and takes up to four weeks to complete the task. The nest is then deserted for several days before the single egg is laid. Again the egg is left for several days before incubation starts. The incubation period takes about six weeks and the chick is in the nest for another six weeks. Not only is the lyre-bird an unusual bird, but it is, in addition, a leisurely one.

Flycatchers

IN THE FUTURE, should you ever be called a thickhead, you can consider it a compliment—if you are ornithologically minded, that is. Thickheads are flycatchers and flycatchers are some of the most attractive and interesting birds to watch. These particular flycatchers are to be found in the Australo-Papuan area and the different species are to be found in Australia, Malaysia, Tasmania and New Guinea and in some oceanic islands.

They have many other names too, such as thrush (which is incorrect), shrike-thrush, tit-shrike, robin and bellbird. These particular flycatchers are large, robust birds, varying in size, some as small as the European flycatchers and others as large as medium-sized crows.

The name shrike which is often attached to them is no doubt derived from the imposing and shrikelike bills. They are chiefly insect-eaters. One kind strips the bark from trees in search of insect larvae, while the crested bellbird not only eats caterpillars, but actually uses them to decorate its nest after disabling them by squeezing.

The rufous whistler is found in Australia. The song is full and rich and some say it is at its best in the autumn. During territorial displays, it uses what has been described as a whipcrack song. The plumage is chestnut or rufous, the chin is white and there is a black band passing through the eye to the beak.

The nest is built in an upright fork of a tree up to twenty-five feet from the ground and the frail structure often permits one to see the eggs from the ground. There are usually two or three eggs, brownish in hue, spotted or blotched with dark brown.

Shown here in its usual, eucalyptus woods home in Australia, the male **superb lyre-bird** has sixteen plumes on its tail, the outer pair curved and S-shaped. Lyrebirds are renowned for their extraordinary ability to mimic almost any sound they hear, whether it be the voice of another bird or animal—including man—or the sound of a train whistle or of some machinery.

The scarlet robin is a small Australian flycatcher, only five inches in length, and in no way related to the British or American robin. The vernacular name has been derived from the British species because of its vivid scarlet breast. Apart from this slight similarity, its habits and appearance are quite different and belong to another family. The male bird can be easily identified by the scarlet breast, black head, chest and other upper parts. There is also a small white splash on the wings, and white outer tail feathers. The female is grey on those parts where the male is black, while the red on its breast is paler, and not so extensive.

The cheery trilling song of the male is one of the most enjoyable sounds of the Australian bush. They can also be heard and seen on the roadsides or perching on the telephone wires.

The species is one of the early-nesting birds; the female builds a nest from strips of bark and lines it with hair, feathers or sheep's wool. In this nest, which is normally in a fork of a tree, the hen lays three eggs which are greyish or greenish white thickly spotted with pale brown specks and blotches. The male shares in the incubation of the eggs and in the feeding and care of the young.

White-head

THE WHITE-HEAD (also a flycatcher) is a forest bird of New Zealand which is often called the "bush canary", because it has a pleasant canary-like song in the nesting season, but the most frequent call you will hear from it is the quick "tswit", used incessantly as the small flocks move through the tall forest trees in search of insects for food. In their search they move from branch to branch, then up and down tree trunks, before moving to the next tree to repeat the performance. The white-head is a restless bird, continuously on the move.

Their nests are usually built in the forks of shrubs or small trees where there is plenty of cover. The nest is deep and well built of moss, dry leaves, spider's web, fibres (sometimes wool), and lined with

(bottom left)
Unrelated to the American or British robins and belonging to a different family of birds, the Australian **redcapped robin,** or **scarlet robin,** has all the habits of a flycatcher. It is often seen along the roadsides and in gardens and has a pleasant, trilling song.

(bottom right)
A South American group, the **bellbirds** are often wonderfully shaped and have strange adornments. Some have fleshy beards, others tassels, and some have wattles. The song of the species shown here is like the peal of small bells.

(above, left)
For its winter vacation the **redstart** which has passed a pleasant summer in Europe will make the long trip to Africa. Redstarts build their nests in the holes and crevices of trees. The male has a more varied coloring than the female.

(above, right)
These **dwarf flycatchers** live in woods, especially beech woods in Central Europe, building their nests in the hollow of trees. Most flycatchers are about the size of a sparrow and they mainly eat insects, especially flies, which they grab in the air. The tyrant flycatchers of North America are unrelated to these birds.

(right)
If seen fluttering back and forth between its perch and some point in the air, the **spotted flycatcher** is probably feeding on a swarm of gnats or other insects. This Old World bird can be seen in parklands, orchards and fairly open country. It sings only occasionally and hunts alone.

feathers. Here, three or four creamy or pinkish white eggs speckled with reddish brown are laid, and for about seventeen days the parents share the job of incubation.

Both male and female are almost identical, the male being slightly larger and slightly brighter in hue. They are about six and a half inches in length with head, breast and abdomen whitish brown with back, tail and wing feathers brown.

Mimic Birds

THE MIMIDAE FAMILY is a New World group of birds and nearly all of them are found in the Americas. In appearance they seem to be halfway between thrushes and large wrens. They are long-tailed, have short or rounded wings, and a strong bill which is slightly decurved. They range through North America, South and Central America and the West Indies. The family contains the catbirds, mockingbirds and thrashers. In the Galápagos Islands there is a group of nine

different forms of mockingbirds, which is a good example of how evolution produces species and subspecies in isolation.

Many consider the mockingbird to be the finest songster in the United States. It is at its best during the height of the breeding season. During this period mockingbirds are to be seen fluttering into the air from tall trees, floating on quivering wings and pouring forth their song. They include the sounds of other birds in their vocabulary, as though unsatisfied with their own natural repertoire, and will also sing at night.

Mockingbirds are pugnacious and will attack humans, dogs, cats and large birds to protect their young. They also have an alarm cry which warns nearby birds of approaching enemies.

They are brownish grey above with large white patches on their wings and tail which are most prominent in flight. They are found in the Bahamas, besides most parts of the United States, and were introduced to Bermuda in 1893.

Mockingbirds usually build their nests in thick bramble or hedges situated about ten feet from the ground, although they do sometimes build as high as fifty feet. Four to six bluish green speckled brown eggs are laid.

The catbird received its name from its mewing call, but it is also a fine singer. It can mimic other bird voices, but is not so gifted a mimic as the mockingbird. The catbird with its quiet ways and tameness about the dooryard is one of the most beloved birds in America. Its main diet is caterpillars, beetles, grasshoppers and wild fruits and berries.

The catbird is smaller than the mockingbird, slate-grey all over, with a black cap. When singing, it sometimes, like the mockingbird, perches on the tops of houses, advertising and displaying itself. However, it is more likely to sing hidden in the density of a thicket which is its home.

You will find catbirds' bulky nests of dry leaves, twigs, roots and grasses in bushes, trees and thickets at heights of from four to ten feet from the ground. There are normally four to six eggs, plain bluish green in hue.

Sometimes the brown thrasher is called a thrush, which is quite wrong. It may have the brown plumage and marked breast of many of the thrushes, but there the similarity ends. Thrashers are too long-billed, too long-tailed and too slender to be thrushes. Their evolutionary position is probably somewhere between the thrushes and the wrens. The name "thrasher" is probably derived from their habit of vigorously twitching their long tails when agitated. One bird photographer, with tongue in cheek after receiving a "thrashing" from a pair defending their young, suggested that their aggressive behavior could be the origin of their name. They are indeed bold birds, and will not hesitate to attack anybody or anything which comes too close to the nest.

The song is a succession of short notes and phrases similar to the catbird's song, but more musical and with less of the harsh or nasal notes of the other species.

The thrasher is a slim rufous-red bird, heavily striped below, with a conspicuous yellow eye and, of course, that long tail. It likes the surroundings of thickets and shrubberies. Fruit, berries and insects are its food.

In the middle and northern states, they establish their territories in early spring and, where there is plenty of cover, soon build their loosely constructed nests. Four to five pale blue eggs are laid, evenly covered with small reddish brown spots.

Finches

FINCHES HAVE A WORLD DISTRIBUTION and while many of them have a good singing voice, that of others is poorly developed. They can be classified as seed eaters as this is their main diet, their strong,

In its search for insects and seeds the **towhee,** one of the North American finches, has the habit of noisily and vigorously scratching away leaves under thickets and trees.

(left)
Among the finches are to be found both indifferent musicians and excellent songsters. One of the best known singers is the canary, which is derived from this **serin finch.**

(below)
The various **cardinals** are some of the most colorful of the finches. This striking, crested specimen, for example, is a native of Central America.

Finches feed mainly on seeds and are found all over the world. The **goldfinch** (top left), introduced into North America from Europe, and the **siskin** (top right), common on both continents, have bills with sharp pointed tips which can pick out small seeds from plants. The heavy, powerful bill of the Old World **hawfinch** (above, left), which takes up so much of its face, can exert crushing pressures on the stones of cherries and olives. No less remarkable is the beak of the **crossbills** (above, right), birds that inhabit the pine forests of Europe and North America. The curved, crossing tips are especially suited for extracting seeds from pine cones, the main part of their diet.

generally cone-shaped bills being adapted for extracting and shelling seeds. The size and shape of the beak varies enormously among the different species, according to the type of seeds they eat. The goldfinches of the United States and Europe have more slender bills with a sharp pointed tip used for extracting small seeds from such plants as thistle. The hawfinch has a heavy, powerful bill enabling it to exert crushing pressures of from sixty to one hundred and fifty pounds per square inch on stones of cherries and olives. Then we have the curious crossbill, the tips of whose bills cross, which can extract seeds from the cones of pines.

One finch which sings well is the African yellow-fronted canary, and many Africans keep them as pets so that they can enjoy their trilling song. It is an easy bird to identify, with its bright yellow underparts and grey crown and with the rest of the head marked yellow and black; the back is a dull green with a palish rump that is very noticeable when the bird is flying away from you.

Outside the breeding season, the canary is gregarious, feeding on the ground in flocks of a dozen or more. They are found throughout Africa, in the parks, fields, gardens and grasslands.

The European chaffinch is interesting because it is an excellent example of a species having "dialects" in its song. A few expert ornithologists can identify from which part of a particular country a chaffinch comes by its particular dialect. Marked differences exist between the dialects of chaffinches from different countries and different regions—and even quite small areas will provide dialects found nowhere else. A railway yard with its buildings has been known to provide a sufficient barrier to isolate chaffinch populations, resulting in the development of a local song dialect.

The song of the chaffinch is brief—lasting no more than two or three seconds; but it will be repeated as many as five or nine times in a minute. It is a loud vigorous rattling, to be heard first in February (when it is very noticeable) and finishing about mid-July.

While the name "finch" is often applied to seed-eaters in general, the **wheatear** (top left), sometimes called the fallow finch, feeds mostly on insects. More typical is the **house finch** (top right), also named the crimson-fronted finch or red-headed linnet, a common bird native to western North America but introduced into parts of the East. The females are duller in color and do not sing as well as the males. The rich, rose-colored breast of the male **bullfinch** (above, left) also contrasts strikingly with the grey of the female. Not notable for its song, the bullfinch does not have a clear, piping call and has been trained to whistle tunes. Especially prized for their songs, however, are the domestic canaries, all of which are derived from the original **wild canary** (above, right) of Madeira, the Cape Verde and Canary Islands. The many varieties of coloring and shape are all mutations, created by selective breeding.

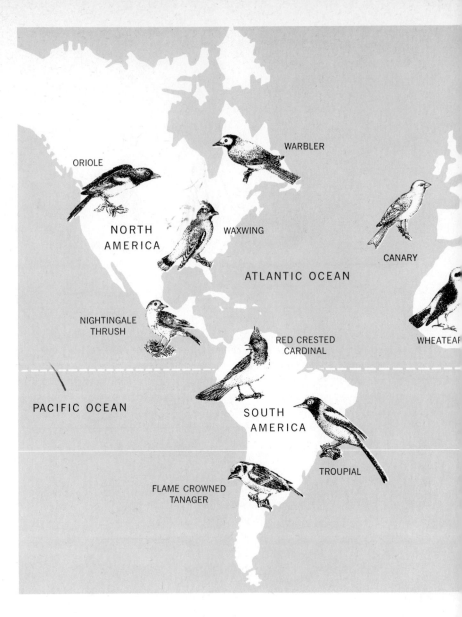

ORIOLE

WARBLER

NORTH
AMERICA

WAXWING

CANARY

ATLANTIC OCEAN

NIGHTINGALE
THRUSH

RED CRESTED
CARDINAL

WHEATEAR

PACIFIC OCEAN

SOUTH
AMERICA

TROUPIAL

FLAME CROWNED
TANAGER

One of the daintiest and brightest of
birds is the **European goldfinch.** A field
of thistle is a good place to see this
bird and to hear its tinkling song. It
also sings in flight.

Most of the chaffinch's food is about seventy-five per cent vegetable matter, consisting of seeds of many weeds, corn, seeds of conifers and fruits. Small amounts of insects are also taken.

The chaffinch is one of the most common of birds in Great Britain, where there are at least ten million of them. For quick identification look for the prominent double white wing bars which both sexes have. The male is more attractively marked than the olive-brown hen, being pinkish brown below, with a chestnut back, greenish rump and blue-grey head. Chaffinches are to be found in such places as hedges, woodlands, gardens, farmlands and can even be seen, on occasion, hopping or walking with short quick steps on pathways or along the roadside.

NIGHTINGALE

GOLDFINCH

THRUSH

EUROPE

ASIA

LAUGHING
THRUSH

SHAMA THRUSH

STRAWBERRY
FINCH

PACIFIC OCEAN

TURDUS
MERULA

·RICA

PARADISE
WHYDAH

JAVA
SPARROW

EMU WREN

INDIAN OCEAN

GOULDIAN
FINCH

AUSTRALIA

SOME TYPICAL SONG BIRDS OF THE WORLD

They breed in rural areas and suburban gardens, and their nests are compact and well built of grasses, roots, wool, moss, lichen and paper and are lined with hair and feathers. There are usually four to five eggs ranging from greenish blue to a brownish with streaks and spots of dark purplish brown. Outside the breeding season they travel in flocks.

Starlings

STARLINGS ARE NOT SINGING BIRDS, but their ability to produce a range of sounds and to mimic—plus the fact that they can be taught to talk—is reason enough for giving them serious consideration. There are about one hundred and ten species in the starling family,

The song of the **chaffinch** is a brief but loud, vigorous rattling which may be repeated at very short intervals. Different kinds of seeds make up the major part of its diet.

which includes such birds as the "talking" mynah of India and the West Indies, and the long-tailed starling of New Guinea which nests in colonies and builds hanging nests; others are the very beautiful superb glossy starling of East Africa and the African long-tailed glossy starling, with a purple and blue flowing tail which reaches fourteen inches in length; then there are the wattled starlings of Ethiopia which move in vast flocks, searching the areas populated by large masses of locusts, and the tickbirds or oxpeckers (which hitch-hike on the backs of game and cattle, cleansing them of parasitic ticks) and also the celebesian starling which has a bill as powerful as a woodpecker's.

They are mostly Old World birds, mainly tropical, and a great many species are to be found in Africa; the largest concentration is in India and the East Indies.

Starlings originally were forest birds, but now they are inhabitants of open country. Their basic food is insects and fruit, but those species which have associated themselves with man will feed on his household scraps and their diet is so varied as to include almost anything—even birds' eggs. They also eat large quantities of what man regards as injurious insects. The Asiatic grey starling feeds on the rice stem borers and is protected in Japan. The rosy pastor starlings eat tremendous quantities of locusts.

Let us now consider the common starling which is such a familiar inhabitant of suburban gardens, large cities and towns. This robust, aggressive and noisy bird became established in many parts of the world. Where man has built, starlings have flourished. Being successful and numerous, they are frequently condemned, but very often without foundation. It is true, of course, that they compete for nesting holes with woodpeckers and bluebirds, but we do not really know if these birds have suffered with the advent of the starling and until extensive research has been carried out, we are in no position to make judgements.

The main complaint against the starling is that the droppings from its large roosting flocks foul buildings and streets. These flocks are made up of many, many birds; 30,000 individuals is by no means an uncommonly large flock, and some are a good deal larger than this. The swarms roosting along Pennsylvania Avenue in Washington, D.C., are believed to exceed 100,000; at least 90,000 have been counted on Duck Island in St. James's Park, London, but then again, we have little proof that they do any definite damage to buildings. Sometimes we just find starlings inconvenient! This is basically the complaint.

Starlings breed (often in colonies) in buildings, holes in trees and nest boxes. They make an untidy nest, mainly of straw and feathers and sometimes leaves, wool or moss. There are usually five to seven pale blue eggs. Breeding begins in April, but it is also known to take place in autumn and winter. Starlings eat all kinds of animal matter—insects, spiders, beetles and earthworms, but also feed on fruit berries, seeds and roots.

The common starling has been introduced to South Africa, North America, Australia, New Zealand and Hawaii and they are widely distributed throughout Europe.

Titmice

THE TITMICE are some of the friendliest, easiest-to-tame and most active of birds. Many of them visit suburban gardens and are regular callers at the bird table. They can be persuaded to breed in nest boxes; tame birds can be taught simple tricks and they have been the subject of intelligence tests.

The name titmouse is of Anglo-Saxon origin. The word "tit" means something small and "mouse" comes from the word "mase", being the Anglo-Saxon description of many small birds. In North America some in the family are called chickadees.

The titmice are mainly woodland birds and feed on insects and other small invertebrates. In the winter months, however, if their normal food becomes scarce, they will readily eat seeds, fruit and berries. Some of the titmice will become regular visitors to a bird table if food is provided for them. Sunflower seeds, nuts, fat, suet and coconut are all relished. On cold winter days a woodland will be full of their lisping calls as a flock moves through the trees, incessantly searching for food. Often they will flock with species such as nuthatches, woodpeckers, creepers and kinglets.

Distributed throughout tropical Africa, the **amethyst** or **violet-backed starling** will nest in any convenient place.

Titmice are generally small, restless and very active birds. Their diet consists mainly of insects, but they may supplement this with seeds, fruit and berries, especially in winter, if other food is scarce. With its white cheek, greenish back and yellow belly, the **great tit** (top left) is a much more colorful bird than the rarer, somber-hued **coal tit** (top right). The **crested tit** (above, left) is easily identified by its white-bordered crest of black feathers, while the larger **bearded tit,** or **reedling** (above, right), has a black stripe of erectile cheek feathers and builds its nest among reeds.

The titmouse family is well distributed but not found in South America, Madagascar or Australasia. Many of the titmice or chickadees are woodland birds, although some of them are found in semi-desert country and often in mountainous areas.

Generally, they are not migratory in the ordinary sense; but a number of northern species do travel several hundreds of miles. Other species are hardy enough to be able to withstand extreme cold. Movements of titmouse populations are sporadic, and usually caused by changes in the food supply situation. However, several species do store food by hiding it in crevices or underneath bark and visit the stores when in need.

The blue tit of Europe does not have a powerful voice, but what it lacks in song it makes up in personality. The song is a liquid trill and there is one very familiar phrase which it uses that can best be described as tsee-tsee-tsee-tsit.

A hole in a wall, a letter box or even a tin can will serve as a nest hole for the **blue titmouse** (top left). This friendly bird can be attracted to a garden if food is provided, particularly sunflower seeds, nuts, fat, suet or coconut. The **long-tailed tit** (center left), on the other hand, builds its nest in the form of a pouch, hidden in bushes. And the male **penduline titmouse** (bottom left) builds an intricately-woven nest, which is suspended from a branch. Unlike most other titmice, which are mainly woodland birds, the penduline tit prefers to live near water. Although they are not migratory in the true sense, titmice move around when there are changes in the food supply situation. Their songs are usually weak.

A **great tit** and **chaffinch** fight over food placed on a tree stump. Great tits are often aggressive and chase smaller birds away from food; but in this instance a chaffinch of equal size and build is holding its own.

A bell-like trill followed by chirping notes is the characteristic song of the **African fire finch.** It is a shy bird, inhabiting the lush bush and rank grasses on the margins of forests and along streams, and disappearing into the cover of undergrowth when disturbed.

The **tanagers** are some of the most picturesque birds to be found in the New World. There are over two hundred different species and most of them, such as this starling-size specimen, are found in Central and South America. They feed on fruit, nectar, insects and spiders.

A regular visitor to the garden, it gives one tremendous pleasure with its acrobatic actions as it swings from a suspended bone or a coconut shell. The blue tit can also be seen in woods, copses, parks, orchards, thickets, and they even visit reed beds. They are found throughout Europe, and in many parts of Asia and Africa.

The plumage of both sexes is the same: a blue crown, the whole side of the face white, back yellowish green and sulphur-yellow underparts. They are only four and a half inches in length. Like the titmice and chickadees of America, they are hole-nesters. They nest in holes in walls, hedgerow banks and in letter boxes, old tins—and nest boxes, when provided. Both sexes help to make the nest, which is of moss and grass lined with hair or feathers, and they have a large clutch—as many as seven to fourteen eggs; nests have been found with up to twenty-four eggs, but such examples probably result from two females laying in the same nest. The eggs are white, speckled or spotted with chestnut.

The smallest of European birds, the **goldcrest** is very similar to the golden-crowned kinglet of North America. It has a high-pitched, somewhat plaintive call.

Although they do attack apple and pear crops, as well as spring buds, they are also voracious eaters of insects and therefore beneficial.

Warblers

Bird names are often confusing, especially if we assume them to give an indication of a bird's relationship and classification. Such is the unfortunate situation we have with the two groups of unrelated warblers of the New and Old World.

Let us consider first the American warblers. These are called wood warblers and are dainty creatures with attractive plumage. Their relationship to other birds is uncertain. On anatomical grounds, they seem nearest to certain tanagers and finches, but in their singing, as the distinguished ornithologist, Oliver L. Austin, points out, "very few of the family can be said to warble in the true sense of the word".

The warblers of the Old World, on the other hand, can indeed warble, many of them having fine singing voices while others have very simple notes. Their nearest relatives in North America are the Arctic willow warbler and several species of gnatcatcher. They are all small, lightweight, rather plain greenish, brownish or greyish birds—(although some of the tropical ones have bright markings)—with fine pointed beaks. They are insectivorous and arboreal in habit, frequenting trees and shrubs, low scrubs, reed beds and grasslands; they move quickly and often quietly through the leaves as they search for insects, spiders and other invertebrates.

Their nests, which are often placed in dense foliage in shrubs, trees, bushes and brambles, may be attached to reed stems or, like those of the tailor birds, inside the fold of a large hanging leaf the edges of which they sew together with plant fibre.

Being insectivorous, they cannot survive in cold climates and are therefore migratory. Most of the European warblers, for example, winter in Africa returning with the arrival of spring. The common and familiar willow warbler, whose liquid song is the delight of summer days, travels to north-west Europe with the coming of warmer weather and arrives in Britain in late March and early April.

One warbler that has proved itself able to survive the winters of Europe is the Dartford warbler; this is a permanent resident of Great Britain, but the exceptionally severe winter of 1962–63 nearly exterminated the entire population. Surprisingly, the blackcap—a summer visitor—has been known to spend the winter in Britain. An investigation a few years ago disclosed that more blackcaps wintered in the country than had been supposed.

The Old World warblers have spread themselves wide and are found throughout Europe, Africa, Asia, including South-eastern Asia (Malaya, Sumatra, Borneo and Java).

The blackcap is a fine singing warbler that leaves Africa to enjoy the spring and summer of Europe. They start arriving at the end of

(bottom left)
An inhabitant of dense, marshy areas of Europe, Asia and Australia, the **great reed-warbler** weaves a purse-shaped nest in the reeds. Its plumage is generally reddish-brown with a lighter underside.

(bottom right)
Not as musical a singer as some of the other Old World warblers, the **willow warbler** is mostly yellow on its underside and greenish above. It builds a spherical nest with a side entrance.

March, but the main wave does not reach the continent until mid-April. The males arrive first and announce their territorial claims with their rich, clear song, which has a remarkable pitch and intensity during this period. They sing from dense cover but tend to use a regular perch from which to deliver their song. When the females arrive, they are extravagantly courted by the males who raise and lower their head feathers, fluff out their body feathers, spread their tail feathers and flap or droop their wings. There will often be courtship chases using a slow-motion flight. Sometimes, even before the female's arrival, the male will perform a dance, consisting of a series of jumps up and down on a branch.

Blackcaps are greyish brown birds; the male has a glossy black cap, and the female a reddish brown one. They like open woodlands and copses with good ground cover of brambles, briars and shrubs. The nest, of roots and grasses lined with hair, is built in hedgerows and brambles by both sexes. There are usually five eggs of buff or stone hue blotched with brown and ashy shell marks. In England, nests are to be found in mid-May or June.

Wrens

TRUE WRENS ARE A NEW WORLD FAMILY comprising nearly sixty species, the majority of which live in tropical America. Only one species, the winter wren, has been successful in bridging the continents and is known in Europe simply as the wren. This particular species has extended its range throughout the great region known as Eurasia.

There are many other birds not members of the family, which are also called wrens in their own areas. We have the wrens of the Australasian regions which are really warbler-like birds and then we have the New Zealand wrens which are so specialized and sufficiently

(bottom left)
The **garden warbler** is one of the two commonest warblers in Europe, the other being the blackcap. Its cup-shaped nest of grasses is built at the base of bushes. It has a sweet, musical song.

(bottom right)
After the winter the male **blackcaps** arrive in Europe to choose their territories. The females come later and are then elaborately courted by the males, who fluff out and spread their feathers, flap or droop their wings, give chase and sometimes perform a dance. Blackcaps feed on insects and have a rich, clear, warbling song.

complex that scientists are undecided as to their affinities with other bird groups.

All true wrens have a similar appearance. The majority of them are under six inches long and the larger species do not exceed nine inches. They are brown or brownish grey, striped, spotted or mottled. They have sharp, slender bills, short rounded wings and carry their tails cocked. They are found in North America, South America, Formosa, Northern India, Africa and the Falkland Islands.

They slip through the tangled undergrowth; forage treeless mountain slopes; search the reeds of salt- and freshwater marshes; haunt the floors of tropical forests and appear suddenly in suburban gardens and shrubberies.

Most wrens build roofed nests but others simply build in cavities. In many cases the sexes share the task of building a nest; the male, however, often leaves to the female the final job of lining it.

The European wren, or winter wren as it is known in America, has a powerful song for its size. This is delivered from a bush, a post or low in the undergrowth and quite often in flight. During the territorial displays, males will face each other and sing vehemently. When this powerful outburst of song does not produce the desired effect of causing one of the males to retreat, then they will fight.

Wrens build their nests in hedges, outbuildings, rock crevices, holes in tree stumps and under the roots of trees.

The nest is well camouflaged with moss, leaves, dead grasses; it is often domed, and has an entrance at the side. The eggs are white, spotted with reddish brown; normally five or six are laid, but larger clutches are by no means rare.

Male wrens often build auxiliary nests which have no connection with the nests built for the incubation of the eggs. The purpose of these false nests is a mystery; it is known that the males roost in them, but it is unlikely that the need to find a roosting place is a sufficient drive to build such nests. A possible theory is that they serve a display function similar to bowers constructed by male bower-birds.

Larks

THE LARKS ARE SMALL, drab birds but what they lack in plumage, they make up for with their superb song. They will pour forth their song either on vibrating wings or from a post or a bush.

The family is almost exclusively confined to the Old World and is best established in Africa, although two species have established themselves in Australia and one (the horned lark) has succeeded in reaching the New World. This attractive species, with its black "whiskers" and "horns", is found throughout North America to southern Mexico and one isolated population is to be found in the Colombian highlands in South America. In Europe it is known as the shore lark.

A species found widely in Australia, the **variegated wren** is not a true wren but actually a warbler. It has a wren-like tail, however, which is held in a cocked fashion.

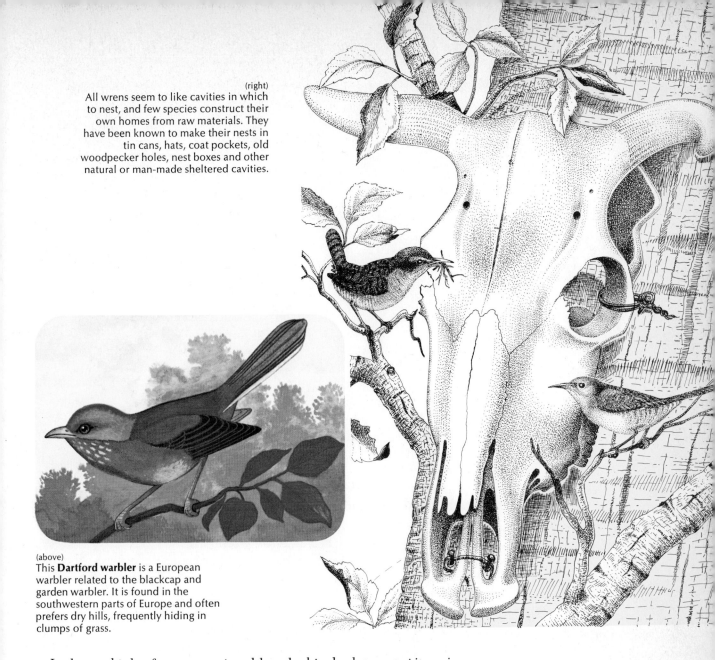

(right)
All wrens seem to like cavities in which to nest, and few species construct their own homes from raw materials. They have been known to make their nests in tin cans, hats, coat pockets, old woodpecker holes, nest boxes and other natural or man-made sheltered cavities.

(above)
This **Dartford warbler** is a European warbler related to the blackcap and garden warbler. It is found in the southwestern parts of Europe and often prefers dry hills, frequently hiding in clumps of grass.

Larks are birds of open terrain, although thin bush-type territory is tolerated, living on plains, moorlands, cultivated fields, deserts or beaches. They are not found in forests, woods or jungle country. They are well adapted for a life on open land, using the sky or a simple bush or post to indicate their territory. They make good use of the protective hues of the plumage; indeed, for a group of birds which live in open country, this must be all important.

When alarmed, a lark will run or fly a short distance, then crouch low before running again. The running speed of some larks is at least five m.p.h.

Their food is vegetable and animal matter, i.e. insects, larvae and seeds. Outside the breeding season, they are gregarious, travelling in flocks of their own kind and sometimes with other species.

(top left)
The rather drab color of its plumage may help to camouflage this **crested lark** in its particular environment. Larks prefer open land, such as plains, moors, cultivated fields, deserts and beaches.

(top right)
Known as the shore lark in Europe, this **horned lark** is the only species of lark in North or South America. It is an attractive bird, with a prominent black collar and small "horns" made of crest feathers.

The skylark is probably the best known of its family and without a doubt, the song flight of the courting male is one of nature's most beautiful sights and sounds. Its beauty and staying power has inspired many poets including Shelley, Wordsworth and Tennyson. Slowly mounting high on quivering wings until all one can see is a mere speck in the sky, almost motionless, the skylark completes the song flight with a sudden, rapid descent. The song itself, normally delivered in the air, is a loud, shrill warbling that lasts as many as five minutes. The skylark sings throughout the year, often starting before daybreak and continuing until dusk.

Skylarks are widely distributed throughout Europe, Russia, Siberia, Asia and China. They are streaky brown with white outer tail feathers, which are noticeable in flight, and a slight crest on the head. They live in open grasslands, cultivated fields, meadows and pastures. The nest is built on the ground, being a primitive structure of dry grasses, where three to five heavily spotted eggs are laid. The hen bird will never directly approach the nest, but will alight some distance away and zig-zag her way to it, thus attempting to mislead any predators that may be watching.

Bower-birds

WHEN THE ENGLISH NATURALIST and one of the founders of ornithology, John Gould, visited Australia between 1838–40, he excitedly described the bower-birds he saw as "extraordinary", "wonderful", "astonishing". It is not surprising that he so freely used such adjectives for he had seen bright-hued birds with loud penetrating voices (they could mimic too) in their unique display grounds, birds that decorated and even painted their bowers!

The bower-birds are restricted to Australia and New Guinea where they are widely distributed. They are primarily forest birds spending

Living mostly in open country, **larks** make use of a simple bush or post—or the sky—to indicate their territory. They are ground-nesting birds, sociable outside the breeding season and fine singers. The most celebrated of its family is doubtlessly the **skylark** (left), which sings throughout the year. Its song is a beautiful, sustained outpouring, usually delivered in the air. Widely distributed throughout Europe and Asia, skylarks are slightly crested and are streaked black and brown above and somewhat paler underneath. They often bathe in the dust on roads and in light soil.

nearly all of their time in trees, except during the courting and display season. In size, they vary between the build of a thrush and that of a crow. Most of their food is fruit but they also eat insects and mollusks.

Their remarkable habit of building bowers is one of the strangest things in nature. The bower is the male's display ground, and is quite separate from the nest which is situated some distance away in a tree. The bowers vary in shape, construction and decoration depending on the species. Scientists have in fact grouped certain species according to the type of bower they build or do not build. Thus we have three distinct groups of bower builders, i.e. the "platform builders", the "maypole builders" and the "avenue builders"—and a fourth group who do not construct bowers.

To decorate their bowers, the birds use a wide variety of objects and substances: fruit, pulp, wet charcoal, flower petals, fungi, beetle wing cases, and they have been known to enter houses to find brightly tinted objects. The bowers are often large; a bower nearly nine feet high is built by one species. It is not surprising to learn that early explorers thought they had discovered playhouses built by native children. The bower is built by the male unassisted, and there he displays until such time as the female is ready to enter the bower for mating. The female builds the nest alone.

The satin bower-bird is probably the commonest of the family in

(below, left)
In almost constant flight to catch flying insects, **chimney swallows** (or barn swallows) do not land on the ground except to collect mud for their nests, which they build on rafters of barns, sheds and sometimes inside chimney stacks. Swallows have pleasant, twittering voices and migrate enormous distances—as much as 9,000 miles!

(below, right)
The **satin bower-bird** is one of a unique bird family that builds display houses, decorating them with bright objects and varied materials such as flower petals, snakeskins, fungi and leaves as well as trinkets taken from houses.

Australia. They are to be found in forests but they also build their bowers in suburban gardens. The first satin bower-bird to be described to science was discovered in France. It was almost certainly taken to that country by one of the French ships returning from Australia.

The bird is twelve inches in length. The male is lilac blue, yet from a distance he looks almost black; the female, on the other hand, is a drab creature, her plumage being mainly blue-grey to olive green. The eyes of the satin bower-bird vary in shade much depending on the bird's emotional state at the time. The iris has been described as lilac, sapphire, blue-violet and dark blue.

This species is one of the bower-birds that paints. During the courting season it will paint the walls of its bower daily and to do this, it uses berries, a piece of bark or charcoal, taken from bush fire debris. Any of these materials it will make into a paste (by masticating it and mixing it with its saliva) which it then applies to the bower walls with its beak. It has been suggested that bower painting is an extension of courtship feeding. In other words the plastering of the walls with a masticated substance is a substitute which satisfies the male's courtship feeding urge without making contact with the female. So far, no other explanation has been offered.

Swallows

THE SWALLOWS AND MARTINS are not accomplished song birds, but their delightful twittering on a spring or summer day is a pleasant, familiar sound.

The swallow family is cosmopolitan with an almost world-wide distribution comprising nearly eighty species. Only the highest latitudes and some oceanic islands are without these birds; but with the exception of the occasional vagrant from Australia, no swallows are found in New Zealand.

(top left)
Bank swallows (or **sand martins**) make their nests in sand banks, in natural holes or in deep, horizontal tunnels that they dig themselves. Like other swallows their wings are long and slender and their tails forked, though much less than the tails of chimney swallows.

(top right)
Mostly soot-colored with a white chin and wings resembling scythes, this **swift** lives almost exclusively in the air and nests under eaves or in tree holes. Although often mistaken for swallows, swifts are not related, and their flight is straighter and faster.

(top left)
The **wood warblers** are found only in the New World, where there are about 120 species. Many of them are migratory. In the autumn the young birds all look the same, which certainly tests the identification abilities of many bird watchers.

(top center)
A crested grosbeak with the characteristic conical bill of a finch, the male **cardinal** is bright red except for a small black area around the base of its beak. Originally a bird of the southern United States, it has pushed its way northwards and is now a common bird in New York State.

(top right)
Visiting gardens and hedgerows on passage, the **willow warbler** has a preference for open woodlands, bushy ground and places with tussocky grass. Its song is simple but extremely sweet. The chiffchaff, another Old World warbler, is almost identical in plumage but has light brown legs instead of blackish and a quite different song.

Generally, they are small birds from four inches to nine inches in length, much of the length being in the forked tail. The wings are long and slender, lending them agility in their almost ceaseless flight in search of flying insects. Their large gapes also assist them in obtaining food in this specialised manner. Their legs are short so that their walk is feeble; indeed, it is no more than a shuffle and the only time they do land on the ground is when they are collecting mud for their nests. They do, however, frequently perch on telegraph wires, twigs, reeds or the edge of their nests.

Swallows are often confused with swifts but they are not related. Swifts have a similar shape—again built for agility in catching insects—but their flight is straighter and less erratic than that of the swallows. They are also faster than swallows; one of the Asiatic swifts is said to fly at two hundred miles per hour; they feed higher in the air and are basically a more primitive group of birds.

Swallows are insectivorous and with their relatively large mouths, catch large beakfuls of insects. If you watch them on a warm summer day when the courtship flight of the queen ants takes place, they will dash and twist through the swarm of ants, snapping them up. One species, the African rock martin, has a special habit of leaving its cliff habitat to visit bush fires, knowing there will be plenty of insects fleeing from the burning grass.

Many swallows construct interesting nests and they are often associated with man. The purple martin of North America nests colonially in tree cavities, but will readily accept man-made houses. The North American tree swallow nests in hollows of trees or nest boxes, while colonies of bank swallows (also known as the sand martin in Europe) dig horizontal tunnels as nests in sand banks and often return to the same banks year after year. The cliff swallow builds its nest on cliff faces and under the eaves of barns. The European house martin usually builds its nest on the outer walls of houses under the eaves and often several nests will be found close together.

The swallows are migratory birds and, being exclusively insect-eaters,

(left)
A slim and graceful bird, the **yellow wagtail** inhabits lowland pastures, water meadows, cultivated fields and marshes. It is yellow and greenish in hue and a spring migrant, arriving in Europe from Africa in late March.

(below)
No one should have difficulty in recognizing the voice of the **phoebe,** since it clearly pronounces its name. This North American flycatcher perches on fence posts or similar sites and sallies forth to catch insects.

(left)
A common North American species, the **chipping sparrow** is to be found around towns and farms. Its song has been described as a chipping rattle or trill.

(right)
One of the most beautiful of the buntings is the American **painted bunting.** When courting, the male spreads his wings and tail and struts before the female. These birds like dense vegetation and are fairly secretive.

(left)
The sharp-tipped, conical bill of the **yellow oriole** is typical of its family. Unlike many other orioles, however, both sexes of this South American species have similar plumage.

they must follow the sun. They travel great distances to do this. The barn swallow, as it is called in America—known simply as the swallow in Britain or chimney swallow in France and Germany—moves in the autumn from Norway to the Cape region of South Africa. In the New World it travels between North and South America, and the Asiatic populations go from the mainland to Malaya and the Philippines.

The barn swallow is the best known of the family and is widely distributed in North America, Europe, Africa and Asia. It is found in open country, especially near water, meadows and arable fields. They are often to be seen hawking for insects over rivers, ponds and lakes.

They are slender in build, long-winged and have forked tails which are longer in the males. The plumage is blue-black on the upper parts, chestnut red throat and the underparts vary from white to pinkish buff. They are seven inches in length.

The flight is light and easy, swerving and banking with regular wing beats and periods of gliding on open or closed wings. In the autumn or at their roosts, they will congregate in large numbers.

The song is a simple, soft warbling and twittering, often in an excited manner, producing a number of short "tswit" notes. They build their nests on rafters of sheds, barns, outhouses and sometimes inside chimney stacks. Both sexes join in building the saucer shaped nest, which consists of mud with pieces of straw for binding. Usually, there are four or five white eggs which are spotted with reddish brown. The breeding season lasts from mid-May until late summer and sometimes into autumn.

The swallow arrives in Europe from far away in Africa at the end of March—a journey of nearly 8,000 miles! A similar journey occurs in the New World when the same species travels between Alaska and Southern Patagonia—a distance of 9,000 miles!

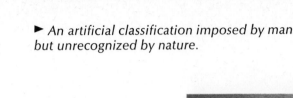

▶ *An artificial classification imposed by man but unrecognized by nature.*

Game Birds of the World

Aᴌᴛʜᴏᴜɢʜ ᴘʀɪᴍɪᴛɪᴠᴇ ᴍᴀɴ was a great hunter his actions never threatened a game bird with extinction. The chief reason for this fact is that early man accepted his natural surroundings as he found them; furthermore, the taking of game was limited because each tribe defended its hunting territories against use by others. In contrast modern man has already wiped out many valuable species of game birds, and continues to threaten many more though he does not depend on them for food.

The blame for this can be largely attributed to his mode of living and the enormous increase in his numbers. His industrial society with its dust bowls, widespread forest destruction and water pollution has destroyed the natural habitat of many species. In addition, until very recently, modern man behaved as though he considered all forms of game to be virtually limitless.

Fortunately, a nucleus of conservationists put a halt to such thinking. The reforms they instituted came too late for a number of important species, but they have succeeded in saving many others through the enactment of intelligent hunting regulations.

The period between the time of the primitive Amerindian hunter and that of the modern conservationist was one of wanton slaughter. It spelled doom to the Labrador duck, the heath hen and the passenger pigeon—all splendid game birds—and many other valuable species, such as the wild turkey, vanished from vast sections of their natural

The classification "game birds" is an artificial one imposed by man on birds hunted for food and sport. Considering them limitless or simply not caring, man has hunted, trapped and in other ways wantonly killed many species, some of which have become extinct.

In more recent times conservation measures and protective legislation have helped to save a number of endangered game birds. (top right) A grouse of the high mountain slopes, the **willow ptarmigan** dons a white dress in winter. The male shown here has already begun to shed its winter plumage. (top, far right) **Red-breasted geese** are the smallest and most strikingly marked of the true geese. They breed in northern Siberia and winter in the Caspian and Aral areas.

range. Apparently initial abundance has little bearing on survival in the face of changing conditions imposed by man.

Certainly many species appeared unlimited in numbers. Reading of the former abundance of game birds, especially in America, the complacency that prevailed becomes understandable. There was really an incredible wealth of "Deere, Conies, Hares, and Fowle". Audubon mentioned flocks of swans so vast they "looked like banks of snow".

However, the reader cannot escape being sickened by the slaughter and the use of every abominable form of trap, including incendiary lures which made it possible to "bag" up to 3,000 Canada geese in a single day. And he cannot but note that there was very little thinking in those days that could be classed as sportsmanlike, at least where guns were used. Some "sportsmen" who didn't have time to hunt game in the wild shot it in the vicinity of New York City. There is a record of 20,000 passenger pigeons being shot in one contest as replacements for clay pigeons!

The reader also cannot escape being struck by the fact that there was apparently no thought of wrong-doing in those days—no enlightenment. Men boasted in their diaries of their bloody exploits, even as had Captain John Smith in 1608: "An hundred and forty-eight fowls the President Anthony Bagnall and the Seriegent Pising did kill in three shots". And later, in just such a climate, the shooting of birds for the market became a respected profession—a business in which professional market hunters openly bragged that their boats nearly sank under the weight of the waterfowl they killed with the massive scatter guns they mounted like cannons to shoot at sitting ducks.

Starting in the late 1800s the senseless mass destruction of game birds in the United States was gradually halted by the passage and enforcement of laws, and many species at the verge of disaster were saved. One important conservation-minded group which aided in this cause was the National Audubon Society. Government game regulations are now operating in most countries of the world. For instance, in the United States the U. S. Fish and Wildlife Service and the game divisions of the various states help to preserve all forms of wildlife.

Completely protected in the United States, the **whistling swan** winters in great numbers at certain places on both the Pacific and Atlantic coasts.

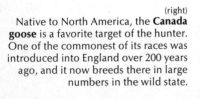

(right)
Native to North America, the **Canada goose** is a favorite target of the hunter. One of the commonest of its races was introduced into England over 200 years ago, and it now breeds there in large numbers in the wild state.

Often the problem of intelligent conservation has been complicated by the fact that many birds cross political boundaries in flying between their breeding and wintering grounds. In North America such problems have been resolved in part by means of treaties between the United States and Canada (concluded in 1916) and between the United States and Mexico (concluded in 1936). The provisions of these agreements are embodied in the Migratory Bird Treaty Act which was ratified in 1936.

Under this Act annual open seasons are set for those migratory birds which may be hunted—geese and ducks, rails, coots, gallinules, snipe, woodcock and (in some states but not all) wild pigeons and doves. In addition the Act gives complete year-round protection to swans, cranes and shore birds which, though classified as migratory game birds, may not be hunted at any time. Turkeys, grouse, pheasants, partridges and quails, being mainly nonmigratory, are protected under the laws of the states in which they occur.

In many European countries large estates still employ "game-keepers" to guard against unauthorized shooting. In Austria a license to hunt is given only after a written and oral examination, involving complete knowledge of each and every wild creature likely to be encountered; skill in the use of firearms and a high standard of field craft ability must be proved. Naturally, the granting of such a license is greatly prized.

In America the Migratory Bird Treaty Act also provides for the study of game bird populations both on their breeding grounds and in the areas where the species are hunted for sport. Much has now been written about game bird management; in Britain an exhaustive study of the red grouse, embodied in a classic report, has done much to give a better understanding of the relation of changes in conditions—both natural and man-made—to the rise and fall in populations. By keeping alert to any change, and with a clearer knowledge of the reasons for it, it is possible to adjust hunting to a safe level and to prevent such disaster as befell the passenger pigeon.

Because of its seeming abundance, the passenger pigeon must have appeared indestructible. Therefore it serves as an object lesson, one that should be recalled frequently. It was in 1876 that a netter observed one of the last great nestings of the passenger pigeon, *Ectopistes migratorius*. The site was in Wisconsin, and the nesting rookery was twenty-eight miles long and some three to four miles wide. The netter noted that a single group of birds arriving at the breeding grounds darkened the sky for five miles. He noted too that the nests were in every tree and that the netters swarmed around the breeding birds using nets, guns, clubs and fire to exploit this mass of birds. Surely they were limitless! Had not Alexander Wilson recorded *two billion* passenger pigeons passing over one spot in Kentucky in 1818? Nevertheless, this incredibly abundant game bird became extinct through lack of protection.

South America is the home of many exotic birds, but few are stranger than the **crested seriema.** It prefers running to flying, its long legs carrying it at great speed over the open grassland. Although not classified as a bird of prey, it feeds largely on small mammals and reptiles.

(top left)
The largest of the perching geese is the **spur-winged goose** of tropical Africa, which often roosts in trees. An adult may weigh twenty-two pounds. Like the related knob-billed goose, it is rather solitary—but not at all shy.

(top right)
Sounded with a closed beak, the call of the **white-winged trumpeter** seems to reverberate from deep within its body. Trumpeters are a small family of only a few species that make their home in the humid Amazonian jungle of South America.

Although the conservationist has made great strides, let no one make the error of thinking the battle is won. To see how far off that day is one has only to look at the 8,000-foot nets in the Great Lakes that have drowned more than 500 diving ducks in a single "haul", or to look at the beaches some November day after a tanker has dumped oil sludge on the sea. On such beaches he will see a "catch" that would probably turn the stomach of even the old-time market hunter: the ducks, geese, gannets, gulls, murres, auks, dovekies, phalaropes huddled in the beach debris slowly starving in their strait-jackets of tar.

Briefly, this is the legacy of game birds that has come down to us. All sportsmen hope the survivors will become even better protected as the years go by, so that those species still with us may flourish for all future generations to see.

To find a satisfactory definition of "game birds" is almost impossible, and the families described are drawn from the list of all the birds of the world which fit the following description: Game birds are birds hunted for sport, birds pursued or taken in hunting, birds stealthy, wary and plucky, fleet of wing and strong of body, birds desirable as food and challenging as targets.

This definition excludes many kinds of birds hunted by primitive men in such places as New Guinea, Africa and Australia, where almost anything that flies, walks, crawls, or swims may be captured for food or adornment.

To the naturalist the classification "game birds" is an artificial one. It is one imposed by man and unrecognized by nature. By the present definition game birds are found in twenty-one of the 174 families that comprise the birds of the world, but some complications naturally arise, since not all birds within these families or even within the genera that make up these families are considered game birds.

Many game species are now fully protected in some countries. In many areas legislation is constantly being enacted to protect more endangered species, but some countries still lack any protection laws whatsoever.

Check list of the orders and families of birds to which the game birds of the world belong.

The figures in parentheses indicate the total number of species in the family.

I. STRUTHIONIFORMES

    1. Ostriches (1)   Family *Struthionidae*

II. CASUARIIFORMES

    2. Emus (1)   Family *Dromiceiidae*

    3. Cassowaries (4)   Family *Casuariidae*

III. RHEIFORMES

    4. Rheas (2)   Family *Rheidae*

IV. TINAMIFORMES

    5. Tinamous (42)   Family *Tinamidae*

GAVIIFORMES (not game birds because of fishy-tasting flesh, but often shot in error)

    Loons or Divers (4)   Family *Gaviidae*

PODICIPITIFORMES (not game birds because of fishy-tasting flesh, but often shot in error)

    Grebes (17)   Family *Podicepedidae*

V. ANSERIFORMES

    6. Screamers (3)   Family *Anhimidae*

    7. Waterfowl (147)   Family *Anatidae*

VI. GALLIFORMES

    8. Guans, Curassows and Chachalacas (38) Family *Cracidae*

    9. Megapodes (12)   Family *Megapodiidae*

    10. Grouse (18)   Family *Tetraonidae*

    11. Quails, Pheasants, Peacocks (174)   Family *Phasianidae*

    12. Guinea Fowls (7)   Family *Numididae*

    13. Turkeys (2)   Family *Meleagrididae*

VII. GRUIFORMES

    14. Button Quails (16)   Family *Turnicidae*

    15. Rails (119)   Family *Rallidae*

    16. Bustards (22)   Family *Otididae*

VIII. CHARADRIIFORMES

    17. Painted Snipe (2)   Family *Rostratulidae*

    18. Plovers (56)   Family *Charadriidae*

    19. Snipe, Sandpipers, Woodcock,   Family *Scolopacidae*
        Turnstones and Surfbirds (79)

IX. COLUMBIFORMES

    20. Sand Grouse (16)   Family *Pteroclidae*

    21. Pigeons and Doves (285)   Family *Columbidae*

The bugle-like call of the **whooper swan** can be heard for a mile or more. This species breeds on the Arctic tundra, far from human interference.

In the following annotated list all of these bird families are discussed and emphasis is given to geographic distribution, behavior, structure and abundance rather than to ther desirability as quarry for the hunter.

A once familiar sight in the open prairies of Southern Europe and Asia, wild **ostriches** survive today only in Africa. These largest of living birds may weigh up to 300 pounds and stand eight feet tall. They are flightless but fast runners on their two-toed "hoofs." Only the male has the ornamental plume and tail.

Ostriches

THE FIRST FOUR FAMILIES on the list of game birds have much in common. They are all large, flightless, and all except the cassowaries are birds of the open prairies. They are fast runners, though reports of speeds of over forty miles are exaggerated. When cornered they defend themselves with their powerful legs. All are prized for their very palatable flesh and for their attractive plumes.

The ostrich is the largest of all birds, standing eight feet tall and weighing up to three hundred pounds—a feast indeed for the emperors of ancient Rome! Hunted by men on horseback, the last Arabian race of ostrich was wiped out as late as World War II. The Arabs hunted

with falcons which harried the large birds until horsemen could catch up with them.

It is the only species of this family which remains today. Formerly it roamed over most of Southern Europe, Asia and Africa. Wild ostriches still live in the veldt of central Africa and are protected in game parks throughout Africa. The cocks assume the responsibility of incubating the eggs and raising the chicks. Strangely enough, for so fierce a bird they take well to captivity and thriving ostrich farms are found today in many parts of the world. As they lay more eggs than the cock can hatch, incubators ensure rapidly increasing flocks. Ostrich plumes find a ready market. Old male ostriches are black and white, females grey and young birds a darker grey.

Emus

THE EMU OCCUPIES the same ecological niche in Australia as the ostrich does in Africa. It stands five feet tall and is the second largest of living birds. Again the male incubates the eggs and rears the young. It has been surprisingly successful in surviving against its main enemy, man. Its habit of breaking down fences and trampling wheat crops resulted in its being declared "vermin" by the Australian government in the early 1930s. It must be one of the very few birds against which machine-gun troops have been dispatched! The war, however, finished in a victory for the birds. Emu-proof fences, five hundred miles long in one part of Australia, now prevent this tough adaptable bird from encroaching on farmland.

Cassowaries

THESE RELATIVES of the emu are rain-forest dwellers and replace the emu in the forests of northern Australia. They are also found in

(top left)
The emu's habit of trampling wheat crops got it in trouble with the government of Australia, the only country in which it is found. **Emus** are the second largest of living birds, standing five feet tall. As with the ostrich, it is the male that incubates the eggs and raises the chicks.

(top right)
A single kick from a **cassowary** has been known to kill a hunter. This relative of the emu has a brightly-colored neck and head with a bony hood on top. It lives in rain forests of Australia and New Guinea.

(above and right)
A South American relative of the ostrich, the **rhea** dodges and weaves as it tries to escape from the mounted cowboy pursuing it. A single male may incubate the eggs and rear the young of six or more females in one ground nest.

(above)
Shy and retiring, the **rufescent tinamou** can sometimes be lured into sight by an imitation of its plaintive whistle. This species is native to Central America.

similar habitats in New Guinea, where they can easily conceal themselves. They have a formidable reputation as defensive fighters; hunters have been killed by a single kick. Cassowaries, of which four species exist, have the head brightly painted in blues, reds and oranges with a casque or helmet on top. Their vestigial wings are simply powerful spines which help to ward off the sharp spikes of jungle vegetation.

Rheas

THE RHEA is the New World representative of the large flightless birds, and is often called the American ostrich. When hunted by horsemen on the pampas of Argentina and Brazil, this fast-running bird will weave and dodge as it runs until it is brought down by the *bolas,* which is to the South American cowboy what the lariat is to the rodeo expert in North America. The rhea is polygamous like his relatives in other parts of the world. He will often have six or more mates who all lay their eggs in a single ground nest, leaving him to incubate the eggs and rear the young. Rheas eat vegetable matter and all kinds of small animals.

This beautifully marked diver is known in North America as the **Arctic loon.** Its loud, haunting call, which some people consider bloodcurdling, echoes and reaches across the shores of the wild northern lakes where it breeds.

Tinamous

THIS STRANGE FAMILY of game birds lives throughout South America. The many species vary in size from quail to large grouse. Their nearest relatives, however, are the rheas, and their resemblance to quail and grouse is an example of parallel development in adaptation to terrain. Their legs and wings are well developed, but they become too quickly exhausted to run very far. They are poor flyers, and when flushed may fly into trees or other obstacles, sometimes even dashing themselves to death. These characteristics are explainable by the abnormally small lungs and hearts of these primitive birds, which usually attempt to elude their attackers by standing still or creeping silently away, aided by their well-camouflaged plumage. Their family life is highly complicated, with a single cock mating with several hens, and raising all the young. Furthermore, one hen will lay eggs in the nests of several males!

Loons or Divers

KNOWN IN THE OLD WORLD as divers, and in the New as loons, these water birds can hardly be considered to be game, since their fishy flesh is unpalatable. Unfortunately for them, they resemble large ducks to the undiscerning hunter and are frequently shot in error. Luckily, they live in isolated, slow-moving waters in summer and are able to get out of danger by diving deeply and staying submerged for long periods. If they have to fly (which they do reluctantly), the flight is fast and powerful once they get into the air. In winter these northern birds migrate to more temperate marine waters, living close to the shore.

(above, left)
The facial ornaments of the **great crested grebe** enhance the courtship display, which resembles a water ballet in which both sexes take part.

(above, right)
Although not good for eating, **grebes**, such as this grey-cheeked variety, are often shot by hunters who mistake them for ducks. Chemical pollution of the ponds and lakes in which they live is another great threat to these fish-eating birds.

Grebes

THIS FAMILY of aquatic diving birds is unrelated to any other known order, and although their flesh is inedible they, like loons, suffer because of a resemblance to ducks and other true game birds. They occupy ponds and lakes visited by hunters who have brought some species to the edge of extinction. Another menace is that of pollution by toxic chemicals; these have radically reduced the numbers of this delightful family, together with many other fish-eating birds.

Many species have beautifully adorned heads and the elaborate courtship displays of such species as the great crested grebe are a wonderful sight. The western grebe, *Aechmophorus occidentalis,* runs across the water like the prima ballerina at an ice show.

Grebes live entirely on the water and build their nests of floating vegetation. They can dive to great depths when disturbed, rising to the surface at a considerable distance. When flintlocks and black powder were used, the grebe could dive so quickly that the flash provided him with enough warning to be underwater when the shot arrived. Because grebes will not take to the air like loons, they are sitting targets rather than sporting shots for hunters. It is hoped that the more enlightened wild-fowlers, who believe in modern conservation, will help to stamp out such unsportsmanlike "hunting" of this inedible bird.

Screamers

THE THREE SPECIES of screamers, all of them inhabitants of South America, are strangely gooselike in appearance, but have very long legs. The best-known is the crested screamer of Brazil and Central Argentina, and it is much prized by local hunters. These little-known birds differ from other families in having small air sacs all over their bodies, to a much greater extent even than pelicans. The exact function of these sacs is unknown. They nest in swamps and the young resemble waterfowl. In flight they often rise high into the air on "thermals" to circle like vultures.

Waterfowl

THE WATERFOWL CONSTITUTE a priceless natural resource. They represent one of the two great orders of game birds—the fowl-like birds on land and the waterfowl. Species from both orders have been domesticated since ancient times, and the raising of them is nowadays a considerable business worth many millions annually. The association of man and waterfowl is so old as to have been recorded in literature at least 2,500 years ago.

147 species of waterfowl, concentrated chiefly in the Northern Hemisphere, have survived the long years of slaughter. Geese, swans and ducks may seem quite different from one another; yet they are structurally very similar. Their three major subfamilies comprise ten tribes: 1) the very primitive long-legged magpie goose of the Australian region, 2) the whistling or tree ducks, with the swans and true geese, and 3) the rest of the world's ducks, comprising seven tribes; shelducks and sheldgeese, dabbling ducks, pochards, perching ducks and geese, eiders, scoters, goldeneyes and mergansers and finally the stiff-tails.

With few exceptions all have short legs and a stubby bill edged with a sievelike arrangement (laminations). The exceptions include the mergansers, which eat fish and have a narrow bill with toothlike edges, and some of the geese, whose bills are modified for shearing grass. The waterfowl mostly gather their food under water. Some tip up and dabble for it; others can dive as deep as a hundred feet and more to take shellfish from the bottom of the sea or to filter small invertebrates and vegetable matter from the bottom mud.

Waterfowl are gregarious, particularly the geese which are, to a large extent, grazing animals. As Captain Jean Delacour has pointed out in his excellent *Waterfowl of the World*, most grazing animals are social.

(below)
While geese are generally confined to the Northern Hemisphere, swans may be found in the colder parts of both hemispheres. They are mostly white, but there are two species of **black swans,** one in Australia and the other in South America (the black-necked swan).

(left)
Like those of other grebes, the nest of the **Slavonian grebe** is a mass of water weeds and decayed vegetation built in shallow water. A depression in the middle receives the eggs. When the grebe is incubating it leaves the nest at the slightest disturbance, but it pulls nest material over the nest before diving into the water out of sight.

After thousands of years of slaughter, 147 species of waterfowl have survived. Most are sociable and gather their food under water or by grazing. One of the rarer waterfowl, pictured here, is the **greater snow goose,** a white goose with black wing-tips. Smaller than the Canada goose, the greater snow goose breeds in the arctic and winters in the bays along the Atlantic coast, from Delaware to North Carolina. On the way it stops each spring and fall at the marshes on the St. Lawrence River near Quebec. An occasional blue goose (in foreground) sometimes accompanies the migration.

An example of this social nature is seen in the great snow goose of North America, of which there are about 42,000 birds still surviving. These birds keep together in one huge flock, migrating as a unit. So tightly does the flock live that at times virtually every bird in existence can be seen from a single vantage point. Most species breed in groups in the northern latitudes, then lose their flight feathers, the entire flock of young and adults becoming flightless for a time. They then can be driven over the ground like a large flock of white sheep. While in this condition, numbers of geese are killed for food by Eskimos.

In swans, and even more particularly in geese, family clans are very closely knit, and the birds may mate for life. Geese live in the Northern Hemisphere, whereas swans are found in the colder parts of both the Northern and Southern hemispheres. Swans sometimes reach more than thirty pounds in weight, and are among the very heaviest of flying birds. The largest swans of all, the trumpeter swans, occasionally have a wing-

(below, left)
Many quilts and pillows are stuffed with the soft, fine feathers, or down, of **eider ducks,** which live in cold northern areas near salt water. Like other sea ducks, eiders are clumsy walkers, but they can dive to depths of at least 180 feet.

(right)
Shoveller ducks stay close to fresh water bordered by grass and rush. They are members of a group of medium-sized, swift-flying "pond or river ducks." Note the long, broad bill and the contrast between the female and more brightly-dressed male.

(right)
An Old World species domesticated for food over nine hundred years ago, the **mute swan** now lives in a semiwild state over much of Europe and parts of North America. Though usually tame, the male or cob fiercely defends the nest in spring, driving away all intruders—man included.

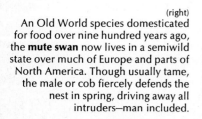

A white cheek patch running under the chin and up the side of the head is the characteristic marking of the **Canadian goose.** Except for this, the head and neck are black, while the rest of the body plumage is grey-brown with a paler breast. Canada geese breed in the cold, northern regions and winter from the Great Lakes to the Gulf of Mexico.

spread of as much as ten feet. Despite their disarming gracefulness, they will fight savagely to defend a breeding territory.

Some ducks, such as the redhead, *Aythya americana*, occasionally lay their eggs in the nests of other ducks, which then foster their offspring for them, and one species, the blackhead duck, *Heteronetta atricapilla* of South America, makes this a regular practice.

Many of the species that have suffered greatly from overhunting are responding to enlightened game management and protection. For example, the trumpeter swan population, which in 1935 was down to seventy-three birds in the United States and a small number in Canada, has now increased to about 1,500 birds. It is hoped that protection will

Buddhist legends dating back to 200 B.C. call the **mandarin duck** a model of fidelity and kindness. Long beloved in its East Asian home, this species figures prominently in Chinese and Japanese art.

enable them to avoid the fate of the Labrador duck, *Camptortynchus labradorium,* a spectacular relative of the eiders; the last live specimen was seen off Long Island in 1875.

With the exception of the Muscovy duck, the mallard is the ancestor of all domestic ducks. It is typical of the swift-flying, buoyant "pond or river ducks" that are found rather abundantly in areas of fresh water almost throughout the world. This group consists of thirty-six species of medium-sized, surface-feeding ducks, nearly all of which have the wing marked with a bright "speculum". Most of the males are more brightly dressed than the females. Among these are the black ducks, the teals, the gadwalls, the baldpates, the shovellers and the pintails. All differ from "sea" and "bay" ducks by having the hind toe only partially webbed. They float high, and rarely do they dive. Their flying speeds range from forty to sixty-five miles per hour. Many of these ducks, which include some of the finest game birds, protect themselves by sleeping in rafts far out in safe waters by day and feeding only at night when hunters cannot see them.

The fourteen species of pochards are freshwater ducks and good divers. This group, consisting of such famous game birds as the redheads, the ringnecks and the scaups, float low in water and obtain most of their food under water. Some, such as the canvasback, *Aythya valisineria*—the most coveted "sporting" duck in America—eat wild aquatic vegetation, and others, such as the greater scaup, eat shellfish.

Scattered widely over the world are the perching ducks, a clan of thirteen species that often perch in trees, and nest in holes in forest trees, sometimes sixty feet above the ground. The beautiful wood duck, *Aix sponsa,* of the New World and the mandarin, *Aix galericulata,* of Asia are two of these. The mystery of how the flightless young reach water shortly after hatching has long been argued. Now we know the adults do not carry them, but instead the downy chicks jump to the ground, landing with a thud and a bounce.

Sea ducks, a clan of twenty-two species, number among their ranks many hardy ducks such as the eiders, scoters and goldeneyes. They are stoutly built, vividly patterned birds that walk clumsily and live mostly in cold northern areas, often near salt water. They feed on small animal life—frequently obtained at surprisingly great depths. One of the smaller ducks is the bufflehead, *Bucephala albeola,* about fourteen inches long. Included in this clan are the common goldeneye, *B. clangula,* and Barrows' goldeneye, *B. islandica,* as well as the old squaw, *clangula hymenalis,* and the harlequin, *Histrionicus histrionicus*—all bright-hued species.

There are four species of eiders living in Arctic waters. The largest is the common eider, *Somateria mollissima,* which, like the others, dives to depths of at least one hundred and eighty feet. Eiders are famous for their down. Almost all species line their nests with down from their own breasts. This serves as a blanket for the eggs when the female is absent

Common today as farm animals, **Muscovy ducks** are, along with turkeys, the only domestic birds which originated in the New World. Both have been carried to virtually every part of the globe. The wild Muscovies are black rather than white on head and breast.

Mallards, pictured here on the Thames at Windsor, are the world's most abundant ducks. Together with the Muscovies, they are the ancestors of all our domestic ducks. Numbers of wild mallards have mated with barnyard escapees to form hybrid populations of comparatively tame birds.

Except for the sharp-pointed tail, **Bahama pintails** do not resemble the larger pintails of the continental United States. They are found in many parts of South America as well as on most of the West Indian Islands.

Most colorful of the North American ducks, the brightly patterned male **Carolina** or **wood duck** reminds one of the equally beautiful mandarin duck. Note the contrast between the male and the much duller-hued female. The forest floor and woodland streams are its usual habitat.

from the nest. In Norway and Iceland down is harvested without disturbing the eggs.

Other sea ducks include the divers known as scoters. The velvet scoter, *Melanitta fusca,* the surf scoter, *M. perspicillata,* and the white-winged scoter, *M. deglandi,* are most commonly seen feeding on shellfish. Though they spend much of the year along the coasts of the Northern Hemisphere, they nest inland next to freshwater ponds.

Included with the sea ducks are birds that chase fish under water, the mergansers. There are seven known species. All have a very narrow bill with toothlike edges that help to hold the slippery prey. Mergansers are true ducks, as proved by the fact that they have the same complex form of breeding rituals. Although their flesh is tainted by their diet, mergansers are regularly hunted in many places, and are often persecuted in the mistaken belief that they deplete fish populations. The common merganser, *Mergus merganser,* which reaches twenty-seven inches in length, is the largest of the three North American species. The most beautiful is the hooded merganser, *Lophodytes cucullatus,* which sports a large black and white crest. In Europe and Asia the pretty black and white smew takes its place.

Another tribe consists of the peculiar stiff-tailed ducks whose legs are so far back on the body as to make walking a barely possible exercise; yet they are the best swimmers among ducks. In North America, the tribe is represented by the ruddy duck, *Oxyura jamaicensis,* which swims in a cocky way, holding the tail nearly straight up, and in Australia by the large musk duck, *Biziura lsbata,* which has a lobe under its bill. They are mainly freshwater birds, and usually of nocturnal habits. Other species are found in East Africa, around the Mediterranean, and over much of South America.

All the farmyard geese, except the Chinese goose, are descended from the **grey goose** of the Old World. In the wild, this widespread species is shy and wary.

As large as a small turkey, the **crested curassow** usually prefers the branches of large trees to the forest floor. Curassows are much prized South American game birds, no species of which has ever been domesticated.

Curassows, Guans and Chachalacas

THIS FAMILY IS FOUND only in the warmer region of the New World. There are twelve species of true curassows, including the great curassow, *Crax rubra,* which weighs ten and a half pounds and, like all members of this group, has a feathered crest. Some species have a solid crest at the base of the bill. These long-legged birds with heavy tails live in the forest, leaping agilely from branch to branch, and sometimes use their wings to half glide or flutter from tree to tree. Their long tails act as stabilizers. Their food varies from fruit, buds and young leaves to small insects and frogs, but although they have long bent claws, they do not scratch the ground like a true pheasant.

All the Cracidae build loose untidy nests of twigs and leaves. These nests, considering the size of the bird, are surprisingly small. There are usually two or three large white eggs, and the young—well feathered when hatched—can fly within three or four days. The parents and young keep together at first, then join with others to form a group of ten or more birds.

Curassows are among the most impressive of all game birds, and abound in some areas of South America. None has ever been domesticated. In this connection, it is perhaps significant that modern man has never succeeded in adding a new domesticated species of bird to those handed down to him by his Stone Age ancestors; yet many of the curassows will associate quite peacefully with barnyard fowl in zoos, and even breed there successfully.

Among the largest species are many birds that have the head richly ornamented. The great curassow is representative of six species of large

Mound-birds, such as the **mallee fowl**, are the only birds in the world to build artificial incubators for their eggs. This species lives in the deserts of Australia.

and highly coveted game birds that occur widely almost throughout Central and South America. The razor-billed curassows have the head decorated with bony helmets that are bladelike, while helmeted curassows have head ornaments that resemble cashew nuts balanced on their foreheads. The male of one species, the horned curassow, has a thick spike sticking up from the crown and looks rather like a unicorn as a result.

Highly prized as game birds, too, are the twelve species of guans and the three piping guans (*Pipile*), which weigh up to about two and a half pounds. The smaller chachalaca, of which there are eleven species, is found as far north as Texas, and weighs only about a pound. The name is derived from their characteristic call. They are often polygamous and form nesting colonies, in which they co-operate in nest-building.

Usually the nest is in a tree, sometimes overhanging the water, but a few species, like *Penelopina nigra* in Mexico, nest on the ground.

Megapodes

The brightly marked **pin-tailed sand grouse** is an African desert species which also inhabits some of the wilder, dry and treeless areas of southwestern Europe. Like other, related species, it is ground-nesting and has very short, feathered legs and toes.

These "incubator birds" differ from all other species in their extraordinary habit of laying their eggs in great mounds of vegetation, earth or sand, allowing the heat generated by the sun or rotting vegetation to incubate the eggs.

Except for one species this family lives in Indonesia, Polynesia, New Guinea and Australia, and replaces their near relatives, the pheasants. There are considered to be only twelve distinct species, of seven separate genera in three distinct groups. The jungle fowl live in the tropical rain forest areas, the brush turkeys in open country, while the best-known species, the mallee fowl, *Leipoa ocellata*, lives in the semi-arid deserts of Australia.

All the megapodes have very large feet which they use to pile vegetation or sand into mounds sometimes ten feet high and as long as fifty feet. The female lays her eggs and then departs; in the case of the mallee

The "drumming" of the male **ruffed grouse** was a mystery until slow-motion photography proved the noise was made by the wings beating against the air.

fowl the number can vary from five to thirty-five. The male stays to look after the "incubator". He can regulate the heat by raising or lowering the height of the mound and is evidently able to judge the temperature by sticking in his bill—perhaps using his tongue as a thermometer. In the morning he will scratch away to allow the interior of the nest to be warmed by the sun, and build it up again in the evening to protect it against the cooler night air. If the interior becomes too warm, judicious reduction of the heap at night permits it to cool somewhat. Some researchers have found that these operations are carried out with such

Grouse live on the ground or perched on large branches in the colder areas of the globe. The largest type is the **capercaillie** (at right), whose name comes from the Gaelic words for "old man of the woods." Other species include the prairie chicken, ruffed grouse, sage grouse, spruce grouse and sharp-tailed grouse.

skill that the incubation temperature never varies by more than two or three degrees!

The eggs hatch at intervals and the chick digs its way to the surface and leaves unaided. It is able to run and fly less than twenty-four hours after hatching and can feed itself immediately, being completely independent of its parents which it may never see. These are possibly the most precocial of all birds. Unlike all other gallinaceous birds, they pass through the downy stage while still in the egg.

Grouse

THE EIGHTEEN SPECIES of the grouse family, with their many subspecies, represent one of the most popular game birds in the Northern Hemisphere. Ptarmigan, prairie chicken and capercaillie are all included in the Tetraonidae. Six genera are confined to the New World, four to the old and one is Holeartic.

These mainly polygamous birds are found chiefly in the colder regions around the world. The ptarmigan change their brown summer plumage to white in the winter and grow dense stiff feathers on their toes to form "snow shoes". All grouse have short wings, but fly very fast for short distances.

In Britain the red grouse, *lagopus Scoticus,* is considered to be the "prize" of all game birds. The large estates in Northern England and Scotland have keepers to tend and protect the birds until August, when the shooting season begins and fashionable parties are held to celebrate the "Glorious twelfth". Huge sums are paid for the first birds of the shoot, which are flown to gourmets all over the world.

The famous ruffed grouse, *Bonasa umbellus,* of North America displays by drumming on a log in the forest. Each male wears rufflike tufts of feathers on its neck. It attracts a mate by its drumming noises; then with its ruff expanded, it struts about, often twisting the forepart of

the body into strange shapes. The spruce grouse, *Canachites canadensis,* is the so-called fool hen, a woodsman's name applied because this bird is so tame as to be very easily captured.

The largest grouse is the polygamous capercaillie, *Tetrac urogallus,* of northern Europe and Asia; it reaches a length of three feet. During its pre-nuptial display this bird of the pine forests becomes so oblivious to outside disturbances that human beings can easily approach within a few feet, but at other times it is very alert and wary. Another very large species of the same region is the black grouse, *lyrurus tetrix,* which has great scarlet excrescences on its head and a beautiful lyre-shaped tail. Some people consider this species to be the most beautiful of all the grouse. The polygamous grouse of the New World—the greater prairie chicken, *Tympanuchus cupido,* the sharp-tailed grouse, *Pedioecetes phasianellus,* both of western North America, and the largest grouse in the New World, the sage grouse, *Centrocercus urophasianus,* are also spectacular. All have extraordinarily developed inflatable display sacs resembling oranges or lemons on the sides of the neck.

These birds of bizarre beauty, treasured as game birds, range up to twenty-eight inches in length, and when the males gather on long-established dance grounds to display like gladiators they make a handsome sight. But the destruction of their habitat has dangerously threatened their numbers, and the eastern form of the prairie chicken, the heath hen, is already extinct.

Quails, Pheasants and Peacocks

WHAT THE FAMILY OF SWANS, geese and ducks is to the water, the pheasants, quails and peacocks are to the land: namely, the most important, valuable and spectacularly beautiful of the game birds. Like many of their aquatic brethren, some of these land birds have been domesticated since ancient times. One, a kind of pheasant, is far and

(bottom left)
About the size of an American robin, the **common quail** is the only species of quail that is found in Europe. These plump, generally insect-eating birds are rarely seen in the open, but the characteristic three-syllable call may be heard day and night.

(bottom right)
The long, forward-curving black feather on the crest of the male **California quail** often helps to identify this bird. This species has a short, thick body and can be found along the coastal regions of California and Oregon.

away the most important bird in the world, and it is no exaggeration to say that there lives hardly a man who has not eaten its eggs and flesh. This species is, of course, the chicken or barnyard fowl, *Gallus gallus*, which still lives as a wild game bird in the jungles of Malaya.

The smallest of the Phasianidae is smaller than a sparrow, and the largest—the most magnificent bird in the world—is the peacock. The Phasianidae are represented by 174 known species, with stocky bodies and longish naked legs and toes. Many of the species have spurs such as are seen on the fighting cock.

Chickens have been bred selectively for three types of birds; food birds, which we all know as the producers of phenomenal numbers of

(below)
Known as the **Hungarian partridge** in America, the Eurasian grey partridge has been imported in huge numbers as game for hunters.

(right)
So brilliant and glittering is the plumage of the **Impeyan pheasant** that it seems to be colored with metallic paints. Such spectacular coloring is typical of other short-tailed Asian pheasants as well.

(below and below left)
A popular and well-known game bird, the **ring-necked pheasant** likes woody plains and damp areas, feeding on grains, small fruit and insects. Once confined to Asia, this common pheasant has been introduced into Europe, North America and many other parts of the world. Because of the multiplicity of stock, there are many differences in the plumage of different varieties, some even lacking the white neck-ring.

eggs, or for themselves as savory items of diet; show birds that rival the pheasants—some in Japan grow tail feathers that reach twenty feet in length; and fighting birds. The ancient sport of cock fighting has been outlawed in many parts of the world as a cruel and savage pastime, but in others it is not only still legal but highly popular. The specially bred fighting cock will fight on against a clearly superior adversary even when mortally wounded.

The New World quails, represented by thirty-six species, are found only in the Western Hemisphere, where they range from the borders of the Arctic to southern South America. The familiar bobwhite, *Colinus virginianus*, the only representative of the family native to the eastern United States, is one of the three bobwhite species that occur widely in America. The northern species is friendly, and it breeds even in city parks. Its young are highly precocious and, like the young of the chicken, are able to run almost as soon as they shake themselves free of the egg. Bobwhites are even more precocious in that they are capable of brief fluttering flights when only a week old.

True pheasants have long tapering tails. The tail of the **Lady Amherst pheasant** (top left) may extend for several feet, and its face may be concealed by its silvery collar of scalloped feathers, as if it were hiding behind a fan. Another beautiful bird is the radiant **golden pheasant** (top right), native to China and Tibet. An amazing courting display is put on by the male **argus pheasant** (center left), which has two enormous tail feathers and many brilliant eye-like spots on its inner wing feathers. It is much less spectacular when the wings are closed, since the general body color is a dull brown. The largest and most magnificent of this family of strikingly beautiful birds, however, is doubtlessly the **peacock** (center right).

(below and bottom left)
News of the **Congo peacock** did not reach western ears until 1936, although it had been familiar to the people of the Congo forests for ages. Its head and body are heavier than the common peacock, while its crest is smaller and its feathers lack eyespots.

This is only one of the methods of protection against predators that the bobwhite has developed. In another, groups of birds sit tails innermost to form a circle in grass or snow. When threatened, they all leap forward, giving the visual effect of an exploding bomb—a device that befuddles even the wily fox.

These birds flush in tight groups, and their rocket-like flights, which consist of sharp flutters interspersed with glides and low zigzagging, make them highly tricky targets and a much sought game. The bobwhite is one of the most common game birds in eastern North America. Other species are the California quail, *Lophortyx californicus*, whose male has a long, black forward-curving crest feather and sixteen species of spotted wood quail of Central and South America. These live on the floor of the forest and are among the most elusive of all game birds.

Pheasants nest on the ground and sleep in trees. Some of the species are highly migratory, such as the common quail, *Coturnix coturnix*, of Eurasia and Africa, which looks very much like a New World quail.

The Phasianidae have been widely introduced over the world. For example, the Eurasian grey partridge, *Perdix perdix*, which is known as the Hun or Hungarian partridge in America, has been imported by the hundreds of thousands to populate hunting areas. This reddish faced bird with generally greyish plumage and barred sides takes to the air with a

(right)
The markings on the male **argus pheasant's wings,** here spread in display, suggest the hundred eyes of the giant Argus of Greek mythology.

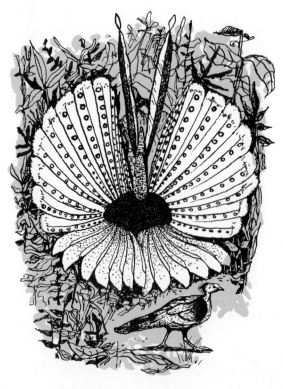

wonderfully rapid take-off which makes it at once the delight and despair of sportsmen.

The quail-like francolins are bright-hued birds usually about a foot long. However, one member of the family, the tiny Chinese painted quail, *Excalfactoria chinensis*, which ranges from Asia to Australia, is smaller than a sparrow.

Some of the pheasants look as if they have been forged out of metal and then coated with metallic paints. One of these is the large Impeyan pheasant, *Lophophorous impeianus*, of eastern Asia; and the many pheasants of the Himalayan regions where the birds are most numerous, such as the blood pheasant, *Ithaginis cruentus*, which is largely crimson and green; or the tragopans, which are so spectacular as almost to defy description. The satyr tragopan, *Tragopan satyra*, is mainly crimson and, like other tragopans, has erectile wattles shaped like horns. These are normally concealed under the feathers of the crown, but when they are inflated during display they stand up like large blue ornaments. The group called fire-backs, which are Indo-Malayan, reach some thirty inches in length. They wear oddly shaped crests, and the pigmentation of their feathers makes them fairly glow.

In yet another galaxy of species are the true pheasants, known to all hunters through the widely introduced ring-necked pheasant, *Phasianus colchicus*, which was first brought to America in 1882 by a relative of Benjamin Franklin. In Great Britain and on the continent of Europe they are artificially reared to stock the large estates, where game laws permit shooting only during the winter season. These hardy birds have a pair of spurs as do all true pheasants, and the male keeps a harem. This is the custom in nearly all species, including the golden pheasant, *Chrysolophus pictus*, the Reeves pheasant, *Syrmaticus reevsi*, and the beautiful Lady Amherst, *C. amherstiae*. The Lady Amherst has a fanlike arrangement of scalloped feathers that is opened over the neck and head, concealing all but the eyes and giving an odd illusion of shyness.

The great Argus pheasant, *Argusianus argus*, of Malaysia performs

(below)
Most popular of the ornamental pheasants is the gorgeous **golden pheasant.** It is closely related to the Lady Amherst pheasant, with which it will hybridize readily in captivity.

(left)
First brought to America in 1882, **ring-necked pheasants** feed largely upon a diet of seeds. These highly regarded game birds are actually hybrids. Their ancestors came from the Near East, Mongolia and Eastern China.

This widely **domesticated** species of **guinea fowl** (right), with fleshy red wattles hanging under its bill, came originally from Africa and nearby islands. Guinea fowls live in grasslands and forest edges in flocks of up to 2000 birds. Male and female are similarly dressed, usually in dark plumage with white spots, bright but featherless heads and necks, and a crest of feathers or a bony helmet on their heads. The **crowned guinea fowl** (below) closely resembles the domesticated species, but it has a longer bony crest on its head.

one of the most bizarre courtship displays known. The male, which reaches six feet in length, fans out vertically his huge flight and tail feathers, especially his immensely broadened, elongated inner wing feathers. These are vividly marked with ox-eye designs, accounting for the bird's Grecian name. So odd is this display that the bird resembles a massive ornament. The performance is given on a specially prepared display ground which the male keeps free of fallen leaves and other debris.

The peafowls are glorified pheasants. Although the males of peacocks might seem too gorgeous to be hunted, they are considered to be fair game in parts of their natural habitat, southern Asia. One could hardly imagine a more ornate bird than a peacock, nor a more spectacular performance than the unfolding of the train and the prancing of a peacock before its mate, accentuated by the audible scrapings of fluttering wings.

The discovery by the late Dr. James P. Chapin of a new peacock on the continent of Africa caused astonishment because all peacocks hitherto known to western ornithologists came from Asia. Yet Dr. Chapin's discovery, which he named *Afropavo congensis,* the Congo peacock, had been hunted for ages by the inhabitants of the Ituri forest! Collector after collector must have narrowly missed this denizen of the deep forest because of its stealthy habits.

Guinea Fowls

IN THE WILDS OF AFRICA, Madagascar, the Comoro Islands and parts of Arabia where the eight to ten species of guinea fowl dwell, as many as two thousand birds may sometimes be encountered in a single flock. Most of the various species look rather like the widely domesticated common guinea fowl, *Numida meleagris.* In only one species is the male provided with spurs.

First domesticated by the Aztecs, the common **turkey** was abundant in the wilds of North America when the first settlers arrived. The type we eat today is the Mexican turkey, brought back to Europe by the Spaniards and then returned to the New World as a domesticated bird by the colonists.

Guinea fowls differ by having the sexes similarly dressed, whereas pheasant males are usually much more splendidly adorned than their hens. In general, guinea hens are deep blue with white spots and bright neck wattles. Often they have helmet-like casques growing from the head. In some species the naked parts of the head are very bright; the smallest of the family, the black guinea fowl, *Phasidus niger,* with its red and pink is an example.

Guinea fowls usually live in grasslands and in the edges of forests, where they build their nests on the ground. They commonly lay up to twenty eggs in a scrape in the ground. They often walk many miles in a day in their search for food. When chased, they prefer to run, but if pressed too closely by a horseman, they spring into flight like giant quail, flying only a short distance and then settling in the top of a tree. There they emit metallic, rasping notes of agitation.

Turkeys

THE LARGEST AND MOST IMPRESSIVE of the New World game birds is the common turkey, *Meleagris gallopavo,* which formerly lived over much of North America southward to the highlands of Central Mexico. Long years of unrestrained slaughter eliminated these magnificent creatures from large areas of North America. Actually the last New England cock was a wise old bird that held out alone for years on a mountain in Massachusetts. When this last member of the true original stock was finally shot, his local fame had reached such a degree that the mountain was renamed Mt. Tom in his memory.

Today turkey farms are located throughout the United States and Europe. The raising of these birds, which were first domesticated by the Aztecs, is now a huge industry. Although the time is past when woodlands abounded with flocks numbering in the hundreds, in some areas of good habitat they have been successfully introduced. These turkeys wandered afoot through the forest, feeding on vegetable matter, particularly on the myriads of acorns, which today most often go to waste.

By a quirk of fate, the early Spanish *conquistadores* brought one game bird, the chicken, to the New World and took back another, the Mexican turkey. The latter was returned to America, probably by the Pilgrims, as a domesticated bird. And it is the Mexican turkey, and the many special breeds thereof, that are eaten at Thanksgiving—birds that go by such odd names as the Bourbon Red and the Beltsville Small White—some weighing nearly forty pounds and others bred to be "apartment-sized" birds, meant especially for small families.

The only other species of turkey in the family Meleagrididae is a spectacular bird of Mexico, Guatemala and British Honduras, but it is a diminishing species, already exterminated over part of its range. It is the ocellated turkey, *Agriocharis ocellata,* which has a bare blue-and-coral head, heavily burred with warts, and one large yellow-tipped protuberance that springs upward from between the eyes. Although much like the common turkey, the ocellated turkey looks brighter and more "metallic".

Both species employ the spectacular display accompanied by scraping noises that is almost too familiar to describe, and both keep a harem of females, defending them from other males; but they take no part in the duties of parental care.

Button Quails

IN TEMPERATE AND TROPICAL PARTS of the Old World are found some species of quail-like birds that have oddly Amazonian habits. The female is larger, more aggressive and brighter than the male, and is the initiator at the time of courtship, using a loud booming call.

The male does the incubating and rears the young in a simple ground nest. This reversal of the usual roles of the sexes is the more unusual

Small groups of **wild turkeys** wander on foot through forested areas, feeding mainly on acorns and other vegetable matter. Conservation measures have helped the much reduced population of these game birds to hold their own in some areas. They may be distinguished from the domestic species by their tail-feathers, the tips of which are chestnut rather than white.

because the female is normally polyandrous, fighting for and winning the attentions of many males during each breeding season, and it is thought she lays several sets of eggs.

The largest of these birds, all of which live in grasslands and flush like regular quail, is about eight inches long. One, the striped button quail, *Turnix sylvatica*, which has an orange breast, reaches the southwestern area of Europe.

Rails

THE RAILS, which comprise the bulk of the 132 species of the nearly cosmopolitan family of rails, gallinules and coots, are among the most elusive of birds and very difficult to approach. All have a highly compressed body—"as skinny as a rail"—and this enables them to run through thick stands of reeds and dash through the tight labyrinths of shafts almost as if by magic. The true rails, of which the clapper rail, *Rallus crepitans*, is a fair example, are so adept at skulking in the marshes that they sometimes manage to live very close to man in comparative anonymity.

Many rails rely so completely on their plumage for protection that they will lie quietly until almost stepped on. They are apt to make long migrations and "lost" birds have reached most areas of the world, so that breeding populations are found even in Iceland and at such remote spots as Wake Island in the middle of the Pacific Ocean. A few of these species are now flightless, and some have become quite large or quite small.

In America perhaps the best-known of the rails is the sora, *Porzana carolina*, which is about eight inches long. This species is less secretive than the others, probably because it has the habit of seeking safety on floating vegetation rather than in the shadows of reed beds.

New Zealand has many large and unusual rails, one of which is the

"As skinny as a rail" is the expression we use, and thanks to their compressed, flattened bodies rails can run quickly through the reeds and stalks of marshes, aided by their four long toes. As with other members of this family, the **clapper rail** (top) is more often heard than seen. A dweller in coastal salt marshes, it is sometimes driven out into the open by high tides. The **black crake** (above), on the other hand, prefers the reeds and sedges along the borders of streams, pools and rivers throughout tropical Africa. Like other rails, it is a poor flyer, preferring to run about on its large feet. Natural camouflage, however, may be the best protection for the **spotted rail** (left), and if approached it is likely to remain still and let its coloring hide it.

chicken-sized weka, *Gallirallus australis*. These birds were once very common, and there are records of a single day of "good" hunting in which two thousand birds were shot. Fortunately, today they are protected, as are other wonderful oddities such as kiwis that still survive on New Zealand. Wekas are noteworthy because, although flightless, they are clever enough to elude pursuing dogs. They enter houses, steal bright objects and are particularly adept at catching rats.

The takahe, *Notornis mantelli,* once thought to be extinct, has recently been rediscovered in some remote valleys in the Murchison Mountains of New Zealand's South Island where it lives in small numbers.

The more aquatic species of the rail family are the gallinules. They are green and wear the bright hues of flowers as head markings, a protective device, for they spend much time on floating vegetation. Gallinules have world-wide distribution in the warmer regions.

The most aquatic of the rails are the well-known coots. Found around the world, even on Andean lakes thirteen thousand feet above sea level, coots resemble ducks and are often shot as game birds, although their flesh is barely edible. They feed by diving, sometimes to a depth of twenty feet.

The American coot, *Fulica americana*, which occurs from Alaska to Argentina, is smoky blue-black, like all coots. The most unusual coot alive today is the Bonaparte's horned coot, *Fulica cornuta*, which builds its own rock islands of potato-sized stones in frigid lakes high in the Andes. On this structure it deposits its eggs. The stone pyramid nests, which sometimes consist of more than a ton of stones, resemble an explorer's cairn.

Bustards

At the beginning of the courting season, male **Australian bustards** grow an apron of skin and feathers, which is inflated with air. They go through fantastic contortions to display their plumes, and at times the apron may drag on the ground.

THESE OLD WORLD BIRDS vary in size from fourteen to over fifty inches long, and one species reaches a weight of thirty-seven pounds —the heaviest flying bird alive today. The twenty-two species of the family are birds of the open plain or desert. Their distribution is discontinuous across Europe eastwards to China, Japan and Australia, with the greatest number living in Africa.

Modern weapons for hunting and man's encroachment into formerly uninhabited open lands have resulted in the extermination of some species. The four-foot-tall great bustard, *Otis tarda,* was last known to breed in Great Britain about 1832. Bustards have long legs and are quite shy, preferring to run and hide rather than to fly, although once in the air they fly rapidly with necks extended forward and legs trailing in the manner of storks.

Also overhunted was the equally tall and slightly heavier Australian bustard, *Choriotis australis,* which once was found in bands of many hundreds. Fortunately, since 1935 when it was in danger of becoming

(left)
Formerly found in open country across Europe and Asia, the large, shy **great bustard** has been driven from much of its former breeding grounds by overhunting and man's encroachment. Unless protected it seems doomed to extinction.

(below)
Bustards are alert but shy, and when disturbed they will usually run and hide rather than fly. They inhabit grasslands and desert regions of Africa, Europe and Asia, have long legs and lack a hind toe. The **little bustard,** shown here, is no more than half the size of the great bustard or the Australian bustard, which is the heaviest flying bird alive today.

extinct, this valuable and picturesque species has been protected by legislation.

Thus it is that today one can see the splendid males displaying to their mates in their age-old and quite unbelievable manner. The male grows an apron of skin and white feathers at the onset of the courting season. Then groups of males gather to display together and thus to compete for mates. The apron is inflated with air, and, when the bird is particularly active, the two-foot-long apron-shaped ornament drags on the ground and sways, while the crest is elevated and the tail is fanned and then folded over the back like a giant hinge.

The female is responsible for nest building, incubating and care of the young, while the male concentrates on mating with as many females as

The widespread **snipe** (right, above) uses its long bill to probe deep into the mud. The North American snipe is known as Wilson's snipe. Its erratic flight often saves it from the hunter's bullets. The **painted snipe** (right, below) form a different group of birds and are gaudier than any true snipe. They are especially noteworthy because the females have a more handsome plumage than the males.

Smaller than its European cousin, the **American woodcock** has a similar spectacular courtship flight and display. Both are beautifully camouflaged, matching a bed of dead leaves.

he can attract. Other species of smaller bustards, such as the lesser Indian bustard, *Syphectides indica,* display alone from special stages, jumping as high as five feet, straight up, so as to be seen over the tall grass that surrounds the dance stage.

In Africa the Kori bustard, *Ardeotis kori,* is often to be found with the bright carmine bee-eater (*Meyops*) perched on its back. The smaller bird dives to catch insects disturbed by the feet of the bustard.

Painted Snipe

IN SOUTHERN SOUTH AMERICA and in the warmer parts of the Old World from Africa to the Philippines and Australia, the hunter occasionally is startled and mystified by flushing a snipe-shaped bird that is richly marked with greens and maroons—altogether different from the true snipe, which is always protectively dressed in a variety of earthy browns.

And, if he watches the female, he will find that she is larger than the male and spreads her wings in a great circle, forming a nearly vertical, bright shield spangled with rich brown markings. She will put on this display for any available male. By comparison with the aggressive female, whose voice is deep and resonant, the voice of the male will sound like a tiny "pip". The difference can be accounted for by the fact that the multiple windings of the female's windpipe are lacking in the male.

The American painted snipe, *Nycticryphes semi-collaris,* and the Old World painted snipe, *Rostratula benghalensis,* are both about ten inches in length, and are more sluggish in taking off and in flying than the true snipe (*Capella*). Quite unlike true snipes, the roles of the sexes in painted snipes are reversed. The female lays the eggs in a nest built by the male, who then assumes all of the duties of incubation and rearing of the young, while the female continues to fight other females for the attentions of other males.

Plovers

RECENT RECLASSIFICATION of this group has cast considerable doubt on which species should be included in this interesting family. Plovers are small to medium-sized birds with long wings and short tails; their nests are mere shallow hollows scraped in the ground. Many of them breed in the Northern Hemisphere, and migrate very long distances to winter in the tropics. The family must be considered to be a mainly tropical one. Twice a year American golden plovers, *Pluvialis dominica,* after nesting in Alaska, travel 3,000 miles across the Pacific to winter in the Hawaiian Islands. This is a typical rather than exceptional example of the fantastic journeys that some species regularly undertake.

Lapwings (*Vanellus*) form a single genus of some twenty-four species. Three are found in North and South America. In Britain the nominated species, *Vanillus vanellus,* is very common, and gathers in large flocks which wheel and turn in formation, uttering a distinctive call from

(bottom left)
An impressive sight is that of millions of **sandpipers** flying southward along a coast during their winter migration. In North America these "shorebirds" are now protected from hunters by law.

(bottom right)
This sociable bird, a **lapwing,** lives in the arctic regions of Europe and Asia and migrates to subtropical zones in winter. Preferring low prairies and pastures, it feeds on worms, mollusks, snails, and insects.

which their common name "peewit" is derived. Other species live in south-east Europe, the Middle East and Africa. The beautiful spur-winged plover, *V. spinosus,* reaches as far as the equator; others, such as the wattled plover, *V. senegullus,* breed only in Africa.

Lapwings with bright wattles, such as the red and yellow-wattled plovers, are common in India; and Australia has three other species.

Golden plovers form a separate group, the European bird, *P. apricaria,* being very similar to the American bird. The black-bellied or grey plover is common to both continents. The New Zealand endemic member of the group is called a dotterel, *P. obscurces.*

Of the sand plovers (*Charadrius*) the best known is the killdeer, *C. viciforus,* whose shrill cry can be heard throughout North America. Some, like the snowy (or Kentish) plover, *C. alexandrinus,* are cosmopolitan, and other members of this group are found from Asia to Australasia.

Some species do not fit into any group. The wrybill, *Anarhyncus frontalis,* of New Zealand is one. The bill of this queer bird is bent to the right. The bird uses its bent bill as a tool for catching the small animals found near and under sea-worn stones and in cracks where a straight bill would be useless.

Snipe, Sandpipers, Woodcock, Turnstones and Surfbirds

ONLY A FEW SPECIES of this large family are still hunted as game birds. In North America, for example, all the sandpipers are now protected by law.

Sandpipers, snipe and woodcock form a family of seventy-seven species of "shorebirds" that are found throughout the world—the woodcock in wooded areas, the snipe chiefly in grasslands and the sandpipers usually along the edge of water. One of the most impressive of all bird migrations is that of the millions of sandpipers that swarm southward following the continental shorelines from their breeding grounds.

All the members of this family fly swiftly in tight flocks, banking and wheeling with great precision. In really great concentrations they can resemble a moving carpet as they run back and forth before the waves in search of the insects, molluscs and crustaceans that form their diet.

Woodcocks, of which there are four species, are among the most highly regarded of all game birds. They are peculiar in having the eyes set far back in the head and in possessing a bill which is sensitive at the tip and can be used to probe the ground like an awl. Even when driven deep into mud, the outer third can be opened to clasp a worm by means of a mechanism that is unique among birds.

Woodcocks are highly migratory. Some species, such as the New Guinea woodcock, *Scolopax rosenbergii,* are nearly black, while others, like the American woodcock, *Scolopax minor,* and the European wood-cock, *Scolopax rusticola,* are the tone of dead oak leaves. As in almost

Long esteemed as a game bird, the **canvasback** of North America is the best-known pochard. It is a good diver, feeding on aquatic plants, especially one known as "wild celery." The male is distinguished by a red head and neck, black breast and bill, and a white back, while the female is mostly greyish.

Until the breeding season, male and female **ruffs** (above, left) live in separate flocks. Then the males grow bright feathers around their necks which they display to attract the females, while engaging in mock fighting among themselves. The females stroll around and select their mates by biting at their necks. Another member of the family of woodcocks, sandpipers and curlews is the common, Old World **snipe** (above, right). A secretive, mostly brown and long-billed bird, it is usually found in marshes and other wet areas. It is easy to distinguish the **curlews** (right) by their typical long, down-curved bills. A group of fairly large birds that live by the seashore, curlews breed in the temperate regions and migrate long distances. Like the sandpipers, they are protected by law in North America.

all the species of this family, woodcocks nest on the ground, with the female doing most of the incubating and brooding.

Near relatives which are equally adept at rocket-like take-offs and evasive flying are the thirteen species of snipe of the genus *Gallinago*. These birds also have the eyes placed farther back in the skull than is usual in birds.

Of eight species of stately curlews the largest, the Madagascar curlew, *Numenius madagarcariensis,* has a wingspread of forty-two inches and a long decurved bill. In North America, where all curlews are now protected, the whimbrel, *N. phaeopus,* is still fairly common, having survived the long years of wanton market hunting that probably accounted for the extinction of its relative, the Eskimo curlew, *N. borealis.*

One species, the upland plover or Bartramian sandpiper, *Bartramis longicauda,* is a large shorebird with a short bill that keeps to inland pastures and has always been highly regarded as a game bird. In North America, however, it is now completely protected.

Other shorebirds live either along the edge of the sea or far inland. One is the very familiar little teeter-tail, the spotted sandpiper, *Acitis macularis*, a seven-inch, dark-brown and white bird that breeds over most of North America.

Other well-known and wide-ranging species are the greater yellowlegs, *Totanus melanoleucus*, and the lesser yellowlegs, *Totanus flavipes*, now completely protected in North America, and many others, too numerous to be more than mentioned here: the tattlers, the willets and the dowitchers to name but a few. Each has its story. The dowitchers (*Limnodromus*), for instance, are peculiar because only the female incubates the eggs and only the male feeds and cares for the young.

Among the members of the snipe family, the ruff, *Philomachus Pugnax*, of northern Europe and Asia is notable for its bizarre breeding habits. Ruffs nest in the tundra of the far north. During the breeding season the males grow special ruffs of bright feathers around their necks. So variable are these that no two of the eleven-inch birds are quite alike. The males always return to display in a tight group on an ancestral display spot, often a little earthen mound. Each bird selects and defends a foot-square spot on the mound. Sometimes twenty birds will take up positions on one arena. Each exhibits its plumes, and there is much fighting. When the males are displaying in this fashion, the hillock resembles a bed of flowers in full bloom.

Ruffs are particularly amazing because males and females live all the

(left)
This pigeon-like bird, the **Pallas' sand grouse,** lives in the steppes and deserts of Asia, where its coloring provides good camouflage from predators. Sand grouse travel far to search for water and will sometimes find their way to Europe, southern Asia and Africa in vast numbers. Most, however, do not survive in the new areas.

(right)
Not a true grouse but a relative of the pigeons, the **chestnut-bellied sand grouse** is a desert bird which flies great distances to find water.

(left)
The plaintive notes of the **mourning dove** may be heard during the mating season all over the continental United States. A relative of the exterminated passenger pigeon, it builds a nest of twigs, forming a flimsy platform that is usually placed in a shrub or low tree.

year in segregated flocks, and the sexes associate for only a few minutes annually. This is when a female becomes interested in the fine show of males, all of which are competing for her attention. She strolls up to, and over, the mound while the males display excitedly; these fall into a kind of swoon one after another, actually collapsing with their bills pushed straight down into the ground. The female selects a mate by biting at his neck, and mating takes place immediately. Then she goes off, builds a nest and rears the young alone.

Along the Pacific coasts of America another strange species, the surfbird, *Aphriza virgata,* is found. This bird breeds on the tops of Alaskan mountains and then spends the rest of the year in and near the spray of beating surf south to Chile. This ten-inch grey and white bird, like its close relatives, the two brightly tinted turnstones, as well as the more aquatic "swimming sandpipers", the phalaropes, has undergone a reversal of parental roles. The males of all these species are the submissive sex and assume all the duties of incubation and rearing the young. All are protected in North America.

The nearly cosmopolitan ruddy turnstone, *Arenaria interpres,* which is named for its reddish-brown and white plumage, hunts food by over-turning beach stones. Occasionally it turns, breaks and devours bird eggs. It also enjoys full protection in North America.

(above)
A member of the American quail family, the **bobwhite** is a popular game bird of the plains from Canada to Guatemala. It owes its name to its clear, characteristic call.

Sand Grouse

IN THE OLD WORLD there occurs a group of sixteen species of semi-terrestrial, pigeon-like birds called sand grouse. These birds, the true pigeons, and certain Estriildine finches, are the only birds that are known to drink with the bill submerged; all other birds lift the bill overhead and let the water run down the gullet. Unlike the pigeons which have fragile skin, sand grouse are very tough-skinned and extremely pugnacious. Ranging in size from that of a street pigeon to that of a small chicken, sand grouse occur all the way from the burning deserts of Arabia to alpine fields fourteen thousand feet high in Asia.

(above, left)
With the dodos and solitaires hunted to extinction, the largest pigeons surviving today are the **Goura,** crowned pigeons of New Guinea. The size of small turkeys, they can raise and lower their beautiful crests of feathers like fans.

(above, right)
The young **wood pigeons,** or **ringdoves,** are fed on a curd-like "pigeon's milk" that is produced from the crop of both parents. These birds are slightly larger than ordinary pigeons and are mostly greyish with touches of white and a wine-red breast.

The best-known species is the Pallas' sand grouse, *Syrrhaptes paradoxus,* of Asia, a fifteen-inch bird that is largely brown with some black-and-white markings. This species periodically departs from its usual range, to invade Europe, southern Asia and Africa in vast numbers. Some of these birds survive to breed in new areas, but most of them perish. The male sand grouse assists in the nest care, but, at night, incubation is the male's responsibility alone.

Sand grouse are extremely wary, fast-flying birds that cover great distances in search of water. When approaching water, they show considerable skill in carrying out movements *en masse,* in order to detect predators and decoy them away.

Sometimes they will drink while hovering over the water and in Africa they have been known to be swallowed up by crocodiles when they descend in great numbers to the water holes, tens of thousands coming together at one time before returning to their desert homes.

Pigeons and Doves

SCIENTIFICALLY SPEAKING, pigeons and doves are indistinguishable, though "dove" is usually applied to the smaller species of this large, world-wide family. They range from sparrow-sized to that of a small turkey. More than half occur in the region from Southern Asia to Australia. All are fast-flying birds that eat fruit, berries, seeds and some insects.

One of the largest groups consists of the bright fruit pigeons of the Old World tropics. Many are green with splashes of "ice cream" tints on the head, neck and breast. The superb fruit pigeon, *Ptilinopus superbus,* is typical. This thrush-sized bird is bright lettuce green, with yellow, pink and purple on its head and neck. Other much larger fruit pigeons gleam all over with iridescent hues. One of these, the sixteen-inch green imperial pigeon, *Ducula aenea,* is largely bronze with crimson feet.

The bleeding-heart pigeon, *Gallicolumba luzonica,* which is white-breasted with a "bloody" spot on its chest, and the emerald dove, *Chalcaphaps indica,* which is a medium-sized bird with shiny plumage, are both widely distributed in the Orient.

The common rock pigeon or rock dove, *Columbia livia,* of Europe and Asia has been domesticated by man for some five thousand years, during which time at least one hundred and fifty very different strains have been produced. Yet if these strains are allowed to interbreed, their progeny revert to the original type which itself is like our common pigeon.

The common pigeon is found in large cities everywhere; either swooping down from the very top of the highest New York skyscrapers to feed on scraps in Central Park, or at Nelson's Column in the heart of London, where passers-by stop to feed them, or a hundred other places. Attempts have often been made to dissuade them from remaining unofficial tenants of man's modern cities, but whatever devices are used, scare guns, electric shock wires, fireworks or recordings of predators' calls, little or no success has been achieved.

Another highly successful species in recent years has been the eastern collared dove, *Streptapelin decaocvo,* which extends its breeding range at a phenomenal rate from Asia across Europe to Britain and within twenty years has spread as far north as Scotland. The wood pigeon, *Columba palumbus,* of Britain is treated as a pest, and shot in huge numbers throughout the year by farmers. Even this has not prevented its numbers increasing in recent years, and it is certainly one bird in no need of protection.

A North American relative that breeds as far south as Mexico and north to Canada is the mourning dove, *Zenaidura macroura.* This twelve-inch, sharp-tailed bird is the only pigeon-like bird that still lives in the cooler parts of North America. Its relative, the passenger pigeon, has been exterminated by man.

The largest pigeons known to have lived were the dodos and solitaires which weighed up to forty pounds, and their story is a sad one. They were hunted to extinction in their island homes near Madagascar, the last perishing some four hundred years ago. The largest pigeons surviving today are three species of crowned pigeons (*Goura*) which live in New Guinea. They are the size of small turkeys and have magnificent crests resembling fine lace. Unless the crowned pigeons are given protection, they seem doomed, for these birds are apparently incapable of defending themselves from mankind.

The magnificent plumage of the **male Indian peafowl** makes it a favorite ornamental bird in captivity. In the wild its raucous voice is used to warn of approaching danger. The "harem" of dull hens disappears as though by magic when they scuttle to safety through the undergrowth.

Birds of Prey

ARE YOU ONE of the fortunate people who have been treated to the sight of a peregrine falcon going into a "power dive" at a starling —or of a harrier, coursing over meadow or moor and then suddenly pouncing on a mouse? Or perhaps you have been privileged to see a large owl sliding silently through the dark woods ever-watching for a rabbit, or have seen a pygmy owl catch and kill a small bird in mid-air, with an astounding display of aerial acrobatics. Possibly you have noted a large snowy owl patrolling a beach, its great yellow eyes gleaming with hunger after a flight from the Arctic. An unwary mole or muskrat has little chance of escape. These are the "snapshots" man is occasionally given—glimpses of birds of prey in their typical activity, as they go about the process of living and feeding.

What Makes a Bird a Predator?

BUT JUST WHAT IS A BIRD OF PREY—a *predator,* to use the scientific term? Simply defined, it means a creature that lives by preying upon and eating other animals. You don't have to look very far to find a predator. What comes immediately to most people's minds is the image of a hawk swooping down on a sparrow. A clear-cut case of predation, without a doubt. But what about the robin that digs an earthworm out of the lawn to fill the gaping mouths of its nestlings, or the nightjar that feeds on mosquitos by the hundreds? If we admit that these are predatory birds, then we must also include the wood-peckers, warblers, swallows, flycatchers, pipits and many, many more

Strictly speaking, birds of prey are those which kill other animals for food, although the term is usually reserved for the eagles, hawks, owls and vultures. Not only do these predators kill quickly and without causing unnecessary suffering, but their activities are also a natural check on their prey, maintaining a balance between population and food supply. It is hypocritical, then, that man—often a wanton killer and a flesh-eater himself—should be so quick to condemn these birds. (right, above) A **lesser grey shrike** impales surplus prey on thorns for future meals. It is unusual in that it habitually nests along roadsides.

of the so-called "beneficial" birds. They all live, wholly or partly, on the large and small animals which they kill. Strictly speaking a great many of our songbirds *are* predators, although we usually reserve the term for the eagles, hawks, owls and vultures.

Why do some people label these particular groups of birds as criminals—and often destroy them as enemies? Surely it is because they make the error of applying human moral standards to wildlife. Because it is accepted as wrong for a man to kill a man, some people reason that it must be hardly less wrong for a bird to kill a bird.

We fail to recognize that civilized man, through his thinking powers, has freed himself from the need for going out and personally killing his own animal food. His substitute system is the breeding of beef cattle, the slaughterhouse and the meat market. Man too is a predator once removed.

We cannot expect sparrows and swallows to match our human system—to breed insects systematically for their food! They must hunt, catch and eat their insect food wherever they can find it. If hawks and other natural enemies of the sparrows are reduced or eliminated, too many sparrows may be left, competing for a limited food supply. This means that some of them will starve. Nature's controls, other than predators, are starvation and disease. Doesn't this indicate that we should look with understanding eyes upon the woodland drama in which a kestrel captures a sparrow and snuffs out its life in an instant? Would it be more humane for the bird to meet slow death by starvation or disease?

Each Creature Plays Its Role in Nature's Drama

A LEADING CONSERVATION PHILOSOPHER, Dr. Irston Barnes, presents the case for man's ethics and nature's laws in a very concise statement:

(bottom left)

A **powerful, hooked beak** is typical of birds of prey, such as the vulture (1) and falcon (3). In addition, the upper part of the falcon's beak has a **toothed edge.** Often the eggs of these birds are tinted or spotted (2), providing some protection from other types of predators.

(bottom right)

Characteristic of birds of prey are **sharp, curved talons.** The snowy owl (A) has three visible, feathered toes with short claws, while the barn owl (B) has two naked toes at the front and two at the back of each foot. A day-hunting bird of prey (C) has strong, sharp claws suitable for grasping. And the long, pointed nails of an eagle's talon (D) can pierce a tough hide and kill instantly.

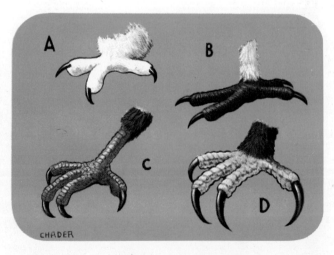

(left)
Unlike other harriers, both sexes of Australia's **spotted harrier** are similarly marked, with a fantastic collection of white or buff dots on a brown or grey background. During courtship the males perform spectacular aerobatics.

(right)
Eagles can be recognized at a great distance by the **flat plane** in which they hold their wings. To determine the species, however, one must look closely at hue and pattern.

(left)
Closely related to the golden eagle, the **imperial eagle** prefers plains, steppes and marshes. It builds a very large nest in a tall tree and consumes great numbers of rodents. This species is found in Spain, southeastern Europe, Central Asia and northwestern Africa. It winters in Africa and southern and eastern Asia.

The **length of the legs** varies considerably among different species of birds of prey, as is apparent from the birds depicted on these two pages. This variation seems to be correlated with feeding habits and the type of terrain the birds normally inhabit.

"In the world of nature," he says, "there are no good and bad birds. Each animal is chained by countless centuries of evolution to an instinctive pattern of action, the most basic of which pertains to the food it eats and the manner of its capture. Thus a hawk is powerless to alter its tastes or its manners. This dictate of nature assures that each form of life shall fulfill its destiny, that no chaos of individual choices shall destroy nature's balance of resources, and that no essential job shall be left undone. The very fact that a form of life exists is clear testimony to its rightness; each form has its essential role in a healthy wildlife community."

(above)

The **African bat hawk** is the only bird of prey with a keeled (longitudinally ridged) beak. It commonly feeds on bats and large insects.

Bird Executions on Fanciful Evidence

A HAWK SOARS over his farmyard and the man with the hoe rushes for his gun. . . . A hunter roaming the October woods flushes a large owl that has been dozing in a tree. He shoots it—and congratulates himself upon having dispatched a "fierce and vicious" killer that he fancies is directly competing with him for grouse and other game. By what logic it is "vicious" for the owl to kill a rabbit, but an act of rugged sportsmanship when the deed is done by a man, has never been very satisfactorily explained. A rancher, surveying his grazing lands from a plane, sights a floating speck in the sky that turns out to be a golden eagle wheeling gracefully, its gaze intent upon a ground squirrel that would make a succulent meal. The rancher recalls lurid tales of eagle depredations of livestock; so he shoulders his gun, draws a bead and the great golden bird plummets earthward. The man in the plane did not thrill to the magnificent powers of flight of the eagle, far more wondrous than those of his mechanical bird. Obviously he would not agree with naturalist Olaus Murie that a dead eagle is both an economic and a spiritual loss.

Another well-known naturalist, Aldo Leopold, expressed it this way: "The swoop of a hawk . . . is perceived by one as the drama of evolution. To another it is only a threat to the full frying pan. The drama may thrill a hundred successive witnesses; the threat only one—for he responds with a shotgun."

Many other birds of prey suffer the same fate as those just described. Vultures are shot by some ranchers because they are suspected of spreading diseases or of killing newborn calves. Even shrikes are sometimes killed because squeamish humans don't like to see them impaling their victims on thorns or barbed wire fences.

We Need the Beauty of Majestic Hawks!

THEN THERE ARE the "bird lovers" who put out feeding stations and proceed cheerfully to slaughter all the "bad" birds that are attracted. They see joy in the face of a chickadee or tit and evil in the visage of every hawk. They apparently feel the Creator slipped up a bit in giving us jays, hawks and owls—and so they are out to improve the wildlife community according to their own design. The distinguished ornithologist and artist, George Miksch Sutton, probably had that philosophy in mind when he wrote, "The public must be brought to a realization of the fact that the soaring of the wide-winged

A small falcon, the **merlin,** or **pigeon hawk,** has a rowing flight that is somewhat like that of a wild pigeon. It seems to be very fond of dragonflies, devouring them in enormous numbers. Not a timid bird, it shows little fear of man.

Distributed throughout most of the world, the **osprey,** or **fish-hawk,** lives near water and feeds on a diet of fish, hovering and then diving feet first to seize its prey. An eagle-like hawk, it is dark above and snow-white below.

hawks, their discordant cries, their mottled plumage and gleaming eyes, are just as truly beautiful as the fluttering flight, cheerful songs and sweet faces of our smaller bird neighbors. Surely, an appreciation of the beauty and majesty of these birds of prey does not demand a special spiritual endowment of some sort! . . . Our deepest, most sincere reasons for protecting wildlife are not, after all, based on economic values. If we can make the public sense the need for these magnificent creatures in everyone's experience, the preservation of the birds of prey which are now too rare will become an important and fascinating feature of the wildlife conservation movement."

Hawks and owls have never had an easy life. Both groups have been persecuted widely; hawks more so than owls, since hawks are day-flying birds. Man is less aware of the activities of the night-flying birds.

Game and poultry farms have had a lot to do with developing anti-predator prejudices. Both the farmer and the game-bird raiser have a cash investment in their charges, and any real or supposed risk of economic loss may cause them to rise up in arms. Also, game-bird farms have inherited some concepts from the days of huge estates and shooting preserves, when the gamekeepers regarded all creatures competing with the game birds as vermin which should be persecuted and destroyed if possible. Fortunately, today more and more people realize the worth of the predators and their rightful place in the wild community. It should be remembered that the open pens in which game farms produce abnormal concentrations of birds are completely lacking in natural "escape cover" such as briar patches, shrubbery and brush piles. This situation allows even the slowest of hawks to dine on birds that are usually too swift for them to capture in a natural environment. Many a gamekeeper bases his generalizations about predation on the special experience of it which is only possible in the highly artificial situation he creates on his game farm.

This African **shrike,** or **butcherbird,** feeds mainly on locusts and other large insects. Its prey may also include snakes, frogs and other birds.

Birds of Prey May Increase Abundance of Game Birds

THE DEVELOPMENT OF WILDLIFE RESEARCH as a profession probably did more than anything to quash the old gamekeepers' ideas about the birds of prey. Professional game managers discovered that the key to wildlife abundance is food and cover. They found that under normal conditions predators exert a negligible influence in determining the abundance of game. They pointed out that many predators actually aid the game by helping to control the populations of rodents which sometimes prey upon the eggs and young of game birds. They testified, too, that predators are responsible for developing alertness and speed in game species, characteristics that most certainly make them more challenging to sportsmen.

Sportsmen have been slow to accept what some of them still regard

(above, left)
Hawk-eagles have a comparatively slight build, but they have strong, hooked beaks and extremely powerful feet. The heavy Asiatic species, which can handle quite large game animals, have been used in hunting for many years.

(above, right)
Able to hover in mid-air like huge kestrels, **short-toed eagles** feed mainly on snakes, lizards and frogs. In certain places their numbers have been greatly reduced by agricultural pesticides.

as impractical theories; but actual experimentation by conservation agencies has proved that the theories are based on fact. There are few game managers today who will deny that, if the environmental conditions are right, game will thrive, and if they are inadequate, game will be scarce regardless of how intensively the predatory birds and mammals are destroyed.

Hawks and Game Thrive Together

BIOLOGISTS AND ECOLOGISTS HAVE noted that in relatively primitive, undisturbed wild areas, both game birds and hawks can be abundant. Careful analysis of the interplay of one species with another in the wildlife community reveals a number of reasons for believing that game and hawk abundance may be linked far more closely than was previously realized.

Sportsmen's organizations which not long ago found it impossible to say anything good about the birds of prey are now speaking up to defend them and urging their members not to kill them indiscriminately. Sportsmen's organizations have gone to the expense of publishing a bulletin on hawks. One concludes with this statement: "Unless any of them (hawks) are doing harm to you—let them go their way in peace. They have their place in Nature and have their appeal to all those who appreciate beauty and adaptation to their mode of life. Do not allow your sympathies for their prey to turn your heart and hand against them. There is more in the predator-prey relationship than meets the eye. Dame Nature fitted them for their role and she is a wise old Dame and knows what she is doing. Don't forget that you, Mr. Man, are the greatest predator of them all, and a wanton destroyer if ever there was one."

Let Nature's Rodent Control Alone—or Else

THERE HAVE BEEN MANY PUBLICATIONS, throughout the years, written with an eye toward educating the public about the value of birds of prey and hopefully preventing them from shooting every one possible. Scientific reports have been published, listing the items that make up the diet of hawks and owls. One such study, published by the U. S. Department of Agriculture, reported the results of studying the stomach contents of 2,690 birds of prey. It concluded that the rodent control activities of the great majority of hawks and owls entitled them to protection at the hands of farmers and others.

Unless we invent some sort of weapon that will eliminate rodents but not men, it is obvious that we will need the predators to help keep the rodents in check. It has been pointed out that one pair of meadow mice could be responsible for one million descendants within a year's time if their fecundity was not disturbed. About twelve thousand tons of vegetable matter would be needed to feed this bustling mouse population. Not only the birds of prey, but a wide variety of mammals, eat mice as a staple food.

How Birds of Prey Help Nature Balance Her Books

BIOLOGISTS HAVE BEEN REITERATING for years that *availability* is the major factor in determining the diet of predators. Because there are many more insects and rodents than anything else, it is not surprising that food habits studies show these to be basic in the diet of

(below, left)
Some scientists cannot decide whether to classify the enormous **lammergeier** as a vulture or as an eagle. It can swallow a lamb's femur whole and uses five-foot sticks in nest building. Persecution by man has greatly reduced its numbers, and the remaining birds are found in remote, high mountain areas.

(below)
Found on the plains and grasslands of central and southern Africa, the **secretary bird** preys largely on snakes, which it batters to death with its feet and wings. About four feet tall and with a wingspan of up to seven feet, it usually prefers walking instead of flying. Its legs are well protected against snakebites.

most birds of prey. A surprising amount of predation on game birds and songbirds, as well as other creatures, is upon what biologists call "surplus populations"—in other words, individuals that cannot be supported by the environment, and would perish whether eaten by the flesh-eaters or not. It is perfectly clear to biologists, but too often not to the hunters to whom they preach, that a game bird or mammal taken by a predator does not ordinarily mean that there will be one less of that species in the game bag next season. The web of life is such a complicated one that biology rather than mathematics must be relied upon.

Because public sentiment usually lags considerably behind scientific research, it is not surprising that legal protection for the birds of prey has been slow in coming. Hawks, owls, eagles and vultures were omitted when most birds were afforded protection by the Migratory Bird Treaty between Great Britain and the United States in 1918 and also in the United States Convention with Mexico in 1936. However, in many inhabited areas of the world there is now some legal protection for most of the birds of prey. Unfortunately, a few communities still adhere to the "kill them all" policy, and more conservation efforts and education are needed. In many regions the *Accipiters,* or so-called "bird hawks", are exempted from protection. This has resulted in very little attempt at enforcing the laws because, generally speaking, the only persons who can distinguish between the protected and unprotected hawks are those who would not shoot them anyway. A violator brought into court simply pleads that he thought he was shooting an unprotected hawk, and usually the case is dropped. Obviously, "unenforceable" laws of this sort, that result in the case simply being dropped, are perhaps worse than no regulations at all. The birds are not protected, the bird-killers are not punished, and much time and money are spent on trying the cases in court. The money and effort could be better applied to enforcing other game laws.

Legal Protection for Hawks Is Weak but Improving

RECOGNITION OF THE WEAKNESSES of present legislation and a more general appreciation of the role of even the "bird hawks" in the general ecology of the outdoors has resulted in the development of considerable sentiment for protection of all hawks and owls. If the public knows it is illegal to shoot *any* hawk or owl, there can be no chance of misidentifying birds, and the number-one excuse of trigger-happy hunters is eliminated.

All-inclusive laws of this type are in force in eleven of the United States and one province of Canada. (Though ten other provinces protect some species.) The golden eagle is protected in Sweden, Finland and the United States. Where the "model" laws are in force, there is usually a clause permitting the taking of protected birds by the farmer

Known as the hen harrier in Europe, the **marsh hawk** prefers to be near water, in meadows or marshes. The male is mostly grey in color and the female brown. The ten species of harriers hunt by day in the same areas that support the night-hunting short-eared owls. Indeed, the two may even share the same roosts.

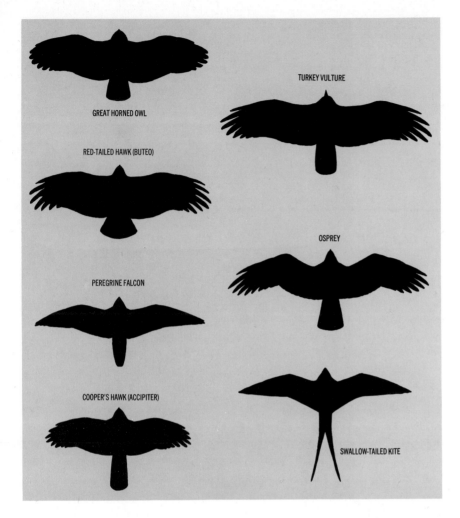

GREAT HORNED OWL

TURKEY VULTURE

RED-TAILED HAWK (BUTEO)

PEREGRINE FALCON

OSPREY

COOPER'S HAWK (ACCIPITER)

SWALLOW-TAILED KITE

A common sight is that of a bird of prey flying overhead, silhouetted against the sky. A distinctive or unique shape often makes it possible to recognize the general type of bird and sometimes even the particular species.

on his own property when such birds are in the act of doing actual damage. This protects the landowner who may suffer from the depredations of those few individual hawks which develop a taste for poultry.

Elsewhere in the world we find varying degrees of protection. In Italy all eagles are considered "vermin", and are shot wherever they can be found—including the national parks. In Japan the golden eagle is killed for its tail feathers, which are used to make arrows. In England this eagle has become extinct, but still holds out in the western part of Scotland, and has bred in Ireland. Legislation, passed in 1954, is still not effectively enforced. There are an estimated 190 pairs of eagles left. Will they survive? No one knows.

The Added Hazard of Migrating

IT IS GENERALLY RECOGNIZED that a high percentage of hawks from widely scattered areas are funneled into fairly narrow flight lanes during migrations. Thus wholesale slaughter of hawks at vantage points

(top left)
One of the commonest birds of prey
in Europe, Africa and Asia is the
buzzard, which preys mostly on small
animals and beetles. It nests in trees
and on rock ledges, has a heavy flight
and a variable plumage. This bird
should not be confused with any of the
New World vultures, which are often
referred to as buzzards in
North America.

(top right)
The **rough-legged buzzard** of the Old
World flies close to the ground,
pouncing on rabbits and small rodents.
A North American subspecies is known
as the **rough-legged hawk.**

along the flyways can nullify much of the protection these birds receive on their breeding grounds. For example, in the United States, certain of the hawks protected by law in Connecticut during the summer can legally be shot in other states through which they pass in the course of their migratory journeys.

To lessen extensive killing of hawks during migration, and to compensate in part for the failure to protect them under the Migratory Bird Treaties, some American conservationists are advocating that all hawks be protected during migrations (September 1 to November 30 and March 1 to April 30) by an Act of Congress. This would be comparable to the federal statute which protects the bald eagle at all times. Except during migrations, hawks would continue to be under the jurisdiction of state laws. It is believed that such legislation would not create the same weight of opposition that could be expected if it were proposed to protect by federal law all hawks at all times. Such legislation could prove an effective means of protecting birds which, at times when they are migrating, are frequently concentrated in quite small geographical areas which may bear little correspondence to any "political" boundaries devised by man.

Despite the fact that many defenders of birds of prey have been doing an outstanding educational job, ignorance about these birds and persecution of them are still almost universal. However, there are many reasons for being encouraged in the belief that things are changing for the better. The tremendous growth of public interest in bird-watching as a hobby means that large numbers of people are afield actively observing the birds of prey. Many go into areas where hawk shooters formerly shot their victims during migration. The shooters feel guilty when bird watchers are around—perhaps because many of them realize that they are violating state laws.

Locally, things can be accomplished quite effectively. Discovery of a hawk slaughtering ground on a prominence in the Kittatinny Moun-

tains of Pennsylvania led to the establishment in 1934 of the Hawk Mountain Sanctuary near Kempton, where shooters previously killed and maimed thousands of hawks and scores of eagles. On a banner day thousands of birds of prey may be observed from the lookout. The early hostility of the nearby residents has turned into open friendliness as a stream of tourists from all over the continent have come to Hawk Mountain—some 12,000 visitors a year! An absorbing account is contained in the Book *Hawks Aloft*, by Maurice Broun, a Director and resident of the sanctuary.

Hawks and owls impress and inspire man; and, when seen close-up, in flight, they cannot fail to do so. But how many men-with-guns consistently refuse to give them this chance—preferring, obviously, to use live targets for their gunnery practice instead of clay "pigeons". Roger Tory Peterson, in his foreword to *North American Birds of Prey*, by Alexander Sprunt, Jr., sums up the situation in these words: "These raptores, of all birds the finest, are like masterworks of art—yet they are subjected . . . to a barrage comparable to that directed at clay pigeons in a shooting gallery. How long would the treasures of the Metropolitan Museum or the National Gallery last if they were treated in such a manner? It is a miracle that our hawks, owls and eagles have hung on as well as they have, but how long can they continue to do so?"

(above)
Masters of the art of soaring, **vultures** can be seen at almost any time, wheeling in tropical skies. The wings are held in a distinct dihedral, forming a **shallow V.**

(top left)
Vultures can stay in the sky for hours, seaching for dead or wounded animals on the ground. Often they can pick out their next meal from a height of 1000 feet or more. The **griffin vulture** pictured here, with its band of narrow, pointed white feathers around its neck, is common in parts of Africa and Asia.

High Praise for the Hawk from a One-time Critic

THERE CAN BE NO DOUBT, however, that public opinion is beginning to move in support of birds of prey. As an example, Bishop Robert N. Hatch, who admits that he once classified all hawks as "big chicken hawks" or "little chicken hawks", has written this eloquent expression of his "conversion":

"To me the hawk is the supreme expression of the amazing orchestra of nature, from which no note can be subtracted without serious consequence to man himself. Hawks are an integral part of that orchestra, as well as an expression of its vast score of checks and balances. They are important to us. When we destroy them through ignorance or sentimentality we release an army of other creatures, like rodents and insects, which was never meant to be released. It would be crass, however, to think of them only in terms of economics. Far more significant are their beauty, their expression of wildness in an age which has lost touch with the things of the earth, and the fact that they are symbols of the whole architecture of God's created world."

Among the birds of prey we find a wide range of sizes, and a great variety of form which often reflects their food-gathering habits. Birds which pursue fast prey must themselves be faster; and those that soar for hours have evolved broad, soaring wings that let them stay aloft with a minimum of effort expended. Typical of the latter group are the vultures.

These are large, usually dark, birds that are commonly seen in temperate and tropical regions. Indeed, it is hard to imagine a view of the African plains or an American desert without one or several of these birds sailing high in the sky. Vultures are experts at soaring

(below, center right)
Familiar to millions of people, the **black vulture** is common along roads, in refuse dumps and ports in the warm regions of the Americas.

(below)
With a wingspan of up to ten feet, the **Andean condor** soars above some of the highest mountains in the world. Its nest is built on rugged cliffs 10,000 to 15,000 feet above sea level, and the young are fed and cared for by the parents until they are more than a year old. Condors, particularly the now rare California condor, have been killed in great numbers by guns and poison.

(right)
The many **vultures of Africa** are invaluable in disposing of carcasses that might otherwise pollute streams and ponds. Some species have weak bills and must wait for others to rip open the skin before they can feed.

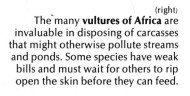

The **Egyptian white vulture** is found in all the Mediterranean countries, southeastern Africa and eastward into India. This small vulture was one of the sacred birds of ancient Egypt and was often represented in sculpture and reliefs. In Africa and Asia it forms part of the "sanitation squads" which clean up town squares as well as the plains and deserts.

flight, and have very good eyesight. They have developed the habit of examining the ground from a height of a thousand feet or more, then landing when they spot a dead or severely injured animal. They have a good working knowledge of thermal air currents, and can stay in the sky for many hours with only a very occasional wing-beat. Their heads are small in proportion to their bodies, and the wing primaries separate in flight, giving a spread-fingered look. The wings of the turkey vulture are held in a shallow V; this dihedral is recognizable from a mile away. The wingspan of the various species of vultures and condors (condors also are vultures) ranges between five and twelve feet. The entire head, neck and crop of a vulture are completely bare of feathers.

(above)
The South and Central American **king vulture** is certainly the most brightly tinted of the world's vultures. In keeping with its royal appearance, it is the first to eat from a newly-found food supply, making other species wait.

(left)
After the Andean and the California condors, the **king vulture** is the largest of the New World vultures. Its brightly-colored head and bizarre appearance set it off from other birds of prey, and especially from the darker, more somber-hued vultures of the Americas.

There are two families of vultures. One, the *Aegypiinae*, contains all the "sanitation squad" of the African plains, which numbers in the hundreds of thousands, and all the other species found throughout Europe, India, South-east Asia and the Himalayas. There are some interesting species. The palm-nut vulture has the odd habit of eating the outer covering of oil and raffia palm nuts, as well as some fish and carrion. The lappet-faced vulture has a bluish grey face, but often blushes pink!

The New World vultures, the family Cathartidae, range from Canada to the southernmost tip of South America. Besides the king vulture, black vulture, turkey vulture and yellow-headed vulture, the family includes the Andean condor, with a wingspan of *ten feet,* and the much rarer California condor, with a wingspan of nine and one-half feet. This bird is in serious trouble. It has managed to hang on in a changing world, when man has pressed ever closer to its remote eyries and shot and poisoned it, often without knowing what he was doing.

Continued in Volume 4

CREDITS
Color photographs and illustrations appearing in this volume were supplied by the following: Photo Researchers, Inc.; The American Museum of Natural History; Armando Curcio; Doubleday & Company, Inc.; U.S. Department of the Interior, National Park Service; and H. S. Stuttman Co., Inc.

Cover illustration and illustrations on pages 262-263 and 297 were photographed at The American Museum of Natural History.